Word Games

Increase Vocabulary through Fun and

Challenging Games and Puzzles!

Grades 1–2

Credits

Author: Janie Schmidt

Production: Quack & Company, Inc.

Illustrations: Carol Tiernon

Cover Design: Peggy Jackson

ISBN 0-88724-955-8

Table of Contents

Introduction

Word Games is a fun way for students to increase their vocabularies, sharpen their spelling skills, and learn some fascinating facts! This book is filled with an exciting variety of games and puzzles that students will enjoy completing. The book features interesting events which occur during the year. The activities complement the events and include specific skills to enhance vocabulary development.

Solving crossword puzzles and word searches, completing analogies, and matching word fragments are just a few of the stimulating types of word-based activities students complete in this book. All words are grade-appropriate, and the activities are sure to improve a variety of language skills.

Students will be fascinated by the information featured in the activities. They will learn about special annual events, such as the Great Bathtub Race in Nome, Alaska, and the Watermelon Fest in Hope, Arkansas. The students will learn about little-known holidays, like National Dessert Day, National Clean Off Your Desk Day, and National Pig Day. The fun, fact-filled activities are sure to motivate them to complete every page.

Whether you want to improve students' language skills or just provide them with meaningful and stimulating word-based activities, *Word Games* is sure to delight and captivate all who complete its pages.

Name _____

Tools of the Trade

Labor Day is celebrated the first Monday of September. It is a day to honor working Americans.

Write the correct letter in each space below using the code.

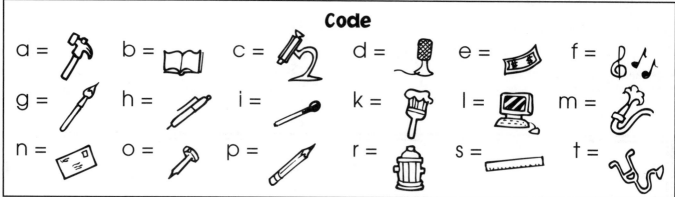

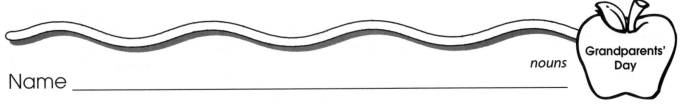

Name _____

Family Tree

The first Sunday after Labor Day is Grandparents' Day. This is the day we celebrate our grandparents by sending a card or giving a hug to show them how much they mean to us.

Circle each word from the Word Bank in the family tree. The words will go across and down.

```
O E N A F A T H A R G
M C C O U M O T H E R
O O L S N O A U N T A
T S G I C T E N S U N
H I R S E A T C I N D
A F A T H E R L C C M
S F N E E T H E T A O
I A B R O T H E R U T
O T A C O U S I N N H
B R R A A A I N H R E
G R A N D F A T H E R
```

Word Bank

BROTHER
GRANDMOTHER
GRANDFATHER
MOTHER   AUNT
FATHER   UNCLE
SISTER   COUSIN

Word Games: Grades 1-2

Name _____

The Great Bathtub Race

Every September in Nome, Alaska, contestants race
down the street in bathtubs filled with sudsy water
for the Great Bathtub Race.

Color each square that contains a letter or letters
that make a word when added to the word family in the bathtub. The
bathtub with all the squares colored wins!

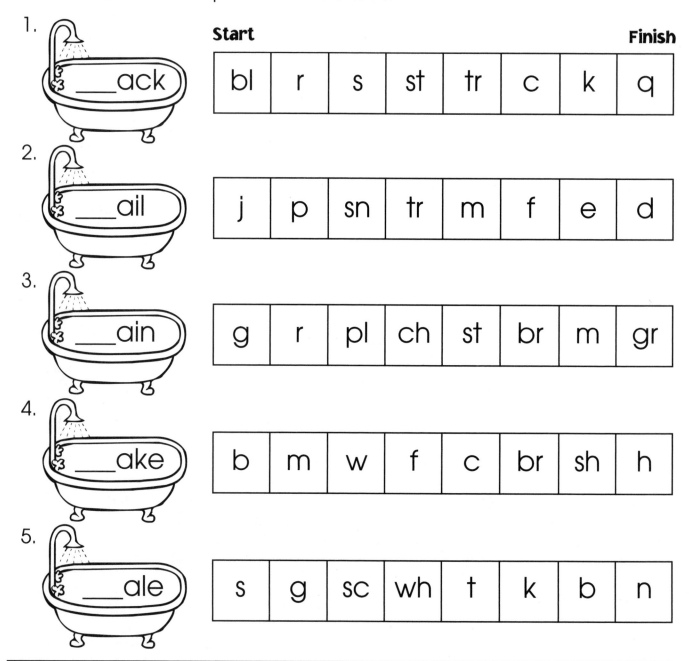

1. ___ack

Start | | | | | | | **Finish**

bl	r	s	st	tr	c	k	q

2. ___ail

j	p	sn	tr	m	f	e	d

3. ___ain

g	r	pl	ch	st	br	m	gr

4. ___ake

b	m	w	f	c	br	sh	h

5. ___ale

s	g	sc	wh	t	k	b	n

National Farm Animal Awareness Week

Baby Farm Animals

Some farm animals have special names for their young. Unscramble the letters to find out the names of the baby animals.

Word Bank

piglet	duckling	colt
calf	gosling	lamb

1. cow   lafc   _ _ ◯ _ _

2. pig   letgip   ◯ _ _ _ _ _

3. goose   insgolg   _ _ ◯ _ _ _ _

4. duck   ukldginc   _ ◯ _ _ _ _ _ _

5. sheep   bmla   ◯ _ _ _

6. horse   tolc   _ _ _ ◯

To find out what a young turkey is called, write the circled letters in order on the blanks below.

_ _ _ _ _ _

American Indian Day

Name _____

Celebrate Native Americans

The fourth Friday in September is American Indian Day. Follow the directions below to discover where some tribes used to live.

Color each space **brown** if the word makes the **long e** sound as in **see**.
Color each space **blue** if the word makes the **short e** sound as in **west**.

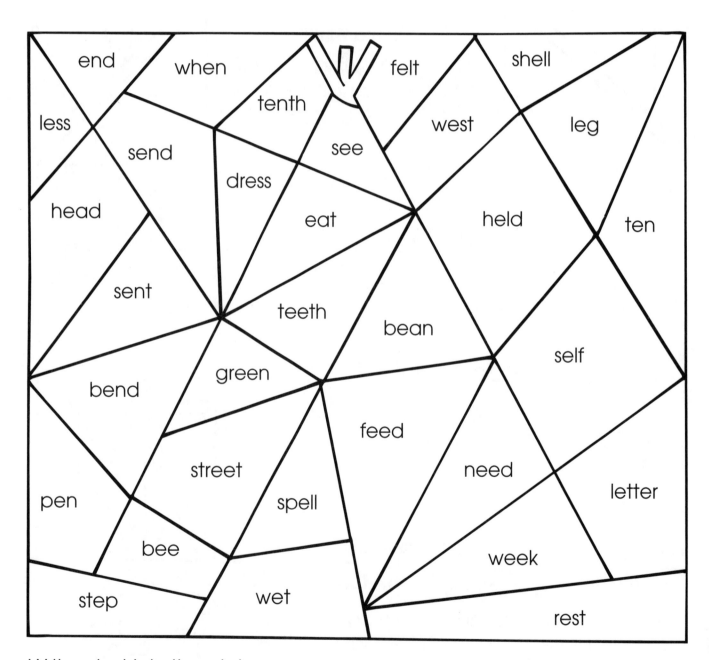

Write what is in the picture. ___ ___ ___ ___ ___

Name _____

Doggy Days

National Dog Week is in September. Dogs are one of the most popular pets in the United States.

Use the picture clues to write words with short vowel sounds.

Write each shaded letter on the matching numbered blank below to solve the riddle.

What do you step in when it rains cats and dogs?

__ __ __ __ __ __ __
1   2   2   4   6   3   5

National
Little
League
Month

Name _____

Let's Hit a Home Run!

Baseball is known as America's favorite pastime.

Step up to the plate and hit a home run by using each clue to complete the puzzle.

Word Bank

notebook headache footstep	raindrop homesick	firewood railroad	outdoors football

1. opposite of indoors

2. a sore head

3. a place to write a note

4. where a train travels

5. a sport

6. missing home

7. footprint

8. wood used to build a fire

9. a drop of rain

Write the letters in the shaded boxes in order on the blanks below to solve the riddle.

Why does it take longer to run from second base to third base than from first base to second base?

When you run from second to third base, there is a

___ ___ ___ ___ ___ ___ ___ ___ ___ in the middle.

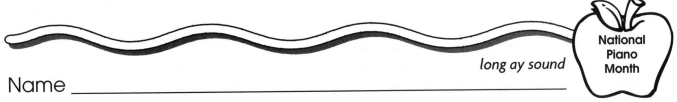

Name _____

You Are Playing My Song!

September is National Piano Month. Did you know that there are 88 keys on the piano? There are 52 white keys and 36 black keys.

Use the code to write **ay** words as in **play**.

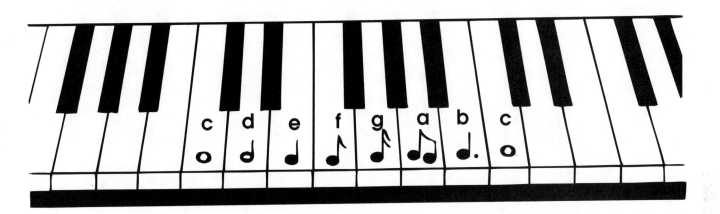

1. ___ ___ y

2. ___ w ___ y

3. m ___ y ___ ___

4. ___ l ___ y

5. ___ r ___ y o n

6. t o ___ ___ y

7. y ___ s t ___ r ___ ___ y

8. ___ r ___ y

9. ___ r ___ ___ w ___ y

Good Manners Month

Name _____

Keys to Good Manners

Are you respectful? Do you treat others the way you want to be treated? Are you polite and courteous? These are all keys to good manners.

Help Andrew find the key to the treasure of the City of Good Manners. Circle the words that show good manners.

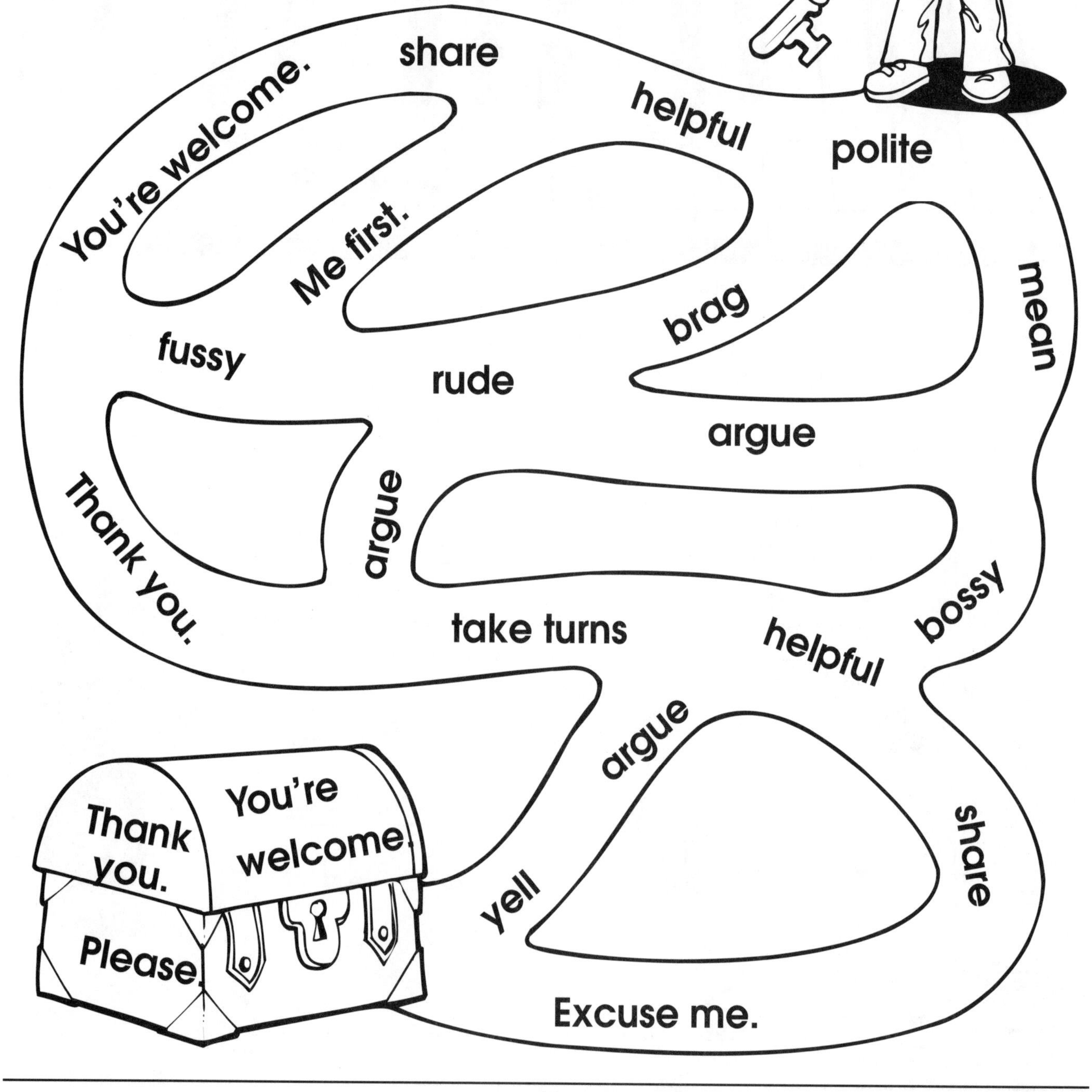

share

You're welcome.

helpful

polite

Me first.

mean

fussy

brag

rude

argue

Thank you.

argue

take turns

helpful

bossy

argue

Thank you.

You're welcome.

Please

yell

share

Excuse me.

12

Name _____

Alphabet Soup

Everyone should eat healthy every day. Healthy eating makes our bodies grow big and strong. Some of the healthiest foods are vegetables.

Make some alphabet soup by unscrambling the vegetable words and circling them in the pot of soup below. The words will go across and down.

1. ractor

_____ _____ _____ _____ _____ _____

2. abnse

_____ _____ _____ _____ _____

3. isonon

_____ _____ _____ _____ _____ _____

4. tatopo

_____ _____ _____ _____ _____ _____

5. orcn

_____ _____ _____ _____

6. kora

_____ _____ _____ _____

7. eleryc

_____ _____ _____ _____ _____ _____

8. spae

_____ _____ _____ _____

p	o	t	a	t	o	x	s
c	k	i	c	k	e	n	c
a	r	b	o	b	a	p	e
r	a	e	r	e	n	e	l
r	a	g	n	a	e	a	e
o	n	i	o	n	s	s	r
t	a	t	o	s	e	p	y

Space Age

On October 4, 1957, the Space Age began with the launch of *Sputnik*, the first man-made satellite.

Unscramble the words in each rocket. Write each circled letter on the blank above the correct number to solve the riddle.

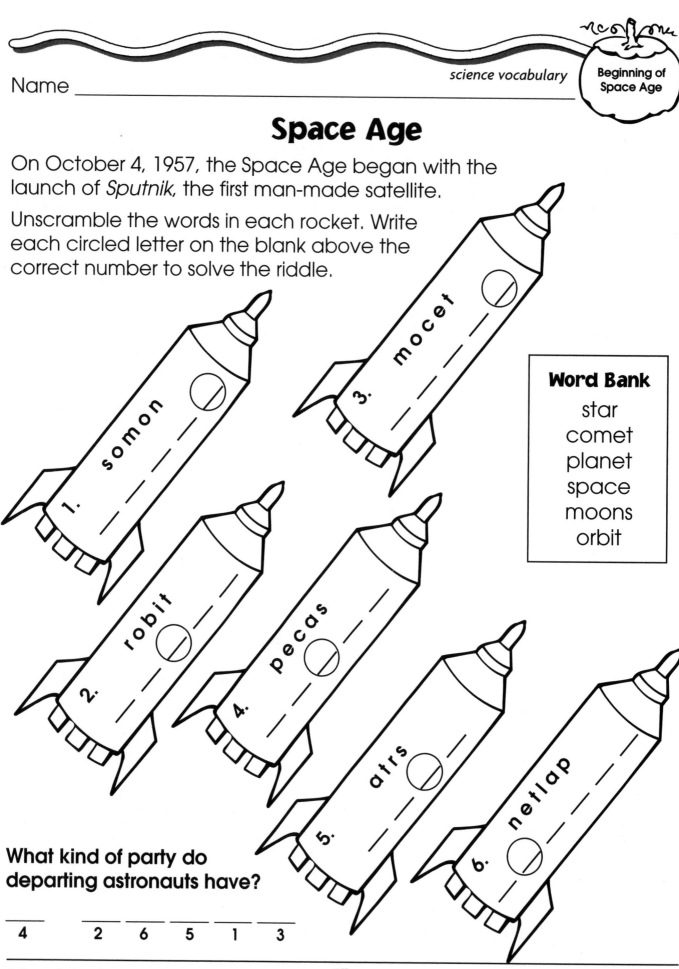

Word Bank

star
comet
planet
space
moons
orbit

1. somon

2. robit

3. mocet

4. pecas

5. atrs

6. netlap

What kind of party do departing astronauts have?

___ ___ ___ ___ ___ ___
 4   2   6   5   1   3

Fire Prevention Week

Name _____

Up the Ladder

The second week of October is Fire Prevention Week. Help Firefighter Fred put out the fire by solving the puzzle.

Start with the word at the bottom of each ladder. Change only one letter to make a new word. You must end up with the word at the top of each ladder.

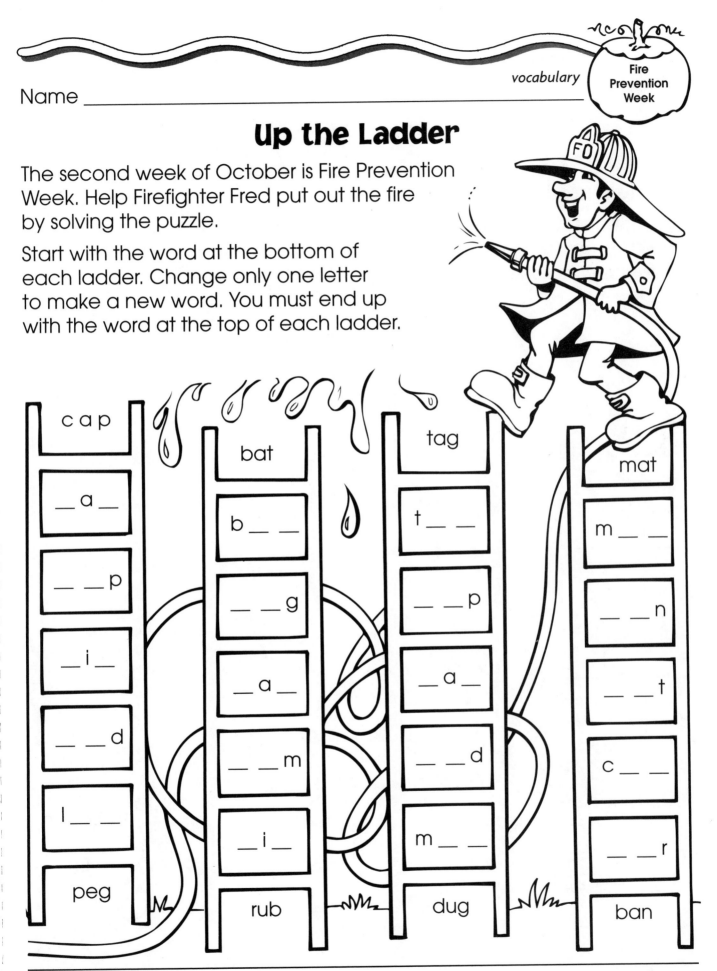

cap

_ a _

_ _ p

_ i _

_ _ d

l _ _

peg

bat

b _ _

_ _ g

_ a _

_ _ m

_ i _

rub

tag

t _ _

_ _ p

_ a _

_ _ d

m _ _

dug

mat

m _ _

_ _ n

_ _ t

c _ _

_ _ r

ban

15

Word Games: Grades 1–2

Name _____

Yum! Yum!

National Dessert Day is in October. Celebrate this day by eating your favorite dessert!

Homophones are words that sound alike but have different spellings and different meanings. Choose the correct homophone for each sentence. Write the correct homophone in the puzzle.

Down

1. Jake _____
   blue, blew
   the whistle.

2. There were
   _____ cookies
   ate, eight
   left.

3. The house was
   made of
   _____.
   would, wood

4. Everyone wants
   world _____.
   piece, peace

7. The boat had a
   _____.
   sail, sale

Across

1. Did you see that
   _____ eat the cake?
   bear, bare

3. Please _____ your name.
   right, write

5. Mary _____ the pie.
   one, won

6. Sally _____ the book.
   red, read

7. Maria _____ the letter.
   cent, sent

16   Word Games: Grades 1–2

Name _____

Flip-Flop, Hippity-Hop

Celebrate National Poetry Day by solving the puzzle. Some poems use words like "Humpty Dumpty" or "Itsy, Bitsy Spider."

Use the Word Bank to fill in the blanks to make a new word. Find the words that you wrote and circle them in the puzzle. The words will go across and down.

1. bow __ __ __

2. ding __ __ __ __

3. see __ __ __

4. tick __ __ __ __

5. ping- __ __ __ __

6. boo- __ __ __

7. fuzzy-__ __ __ __ __

8. piggly- __ __ __ __ __ __

9. walkie- __ __ __ __ __ __

10. splish- __ __ __ __ __ __

clip   *clop*   *clip clop*

Word Bank

splash

wuzzy

hoo

dong

wiggly

tock

wow

saw

pong

talkie

s	a	n	g	d	o	n	g	a
s	w	u	z	z	y	p	o	w
o	i	k	i	e	t	o	c	k
n	g	s	p	l	a	s	h	i
g	g	y	o	i	l	w	o	w
w	l	z	n	g	k	b	o	z
o	y	z	g	g	i	s	a	w
m	o	m	a	l	e	m	e	x

Name _____

Turn It On!

October 21 is Edison Lamp Day. Thomas Edison did not actually invent the lightbulb, but in 1879 he perfected one.

Light up each lightbulb by circling the word that has the opposite meaning of each underlined word.

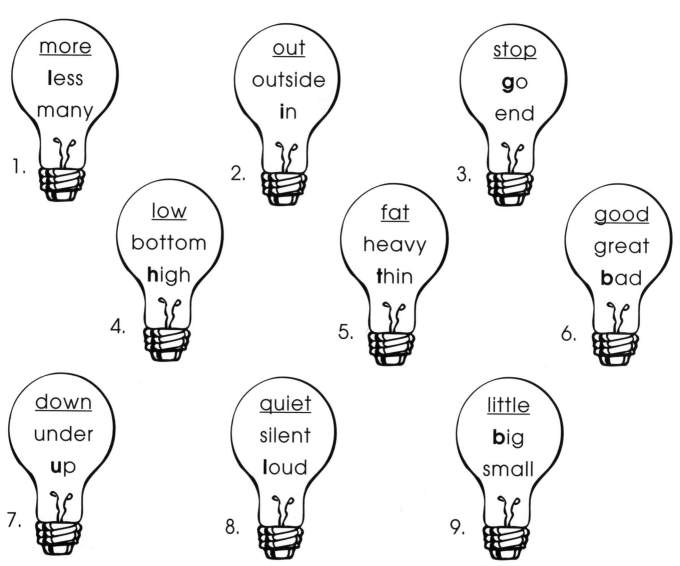

1. more / **l**ess / many

2. out / outside / **in**

3. stop / **g**o / end

4. low / bottom / **h**igh

5. fat / heavy / **th**in

6. good / great / **b**ad

7. down / under / **u**p

8. quiet / silent / **l**oud

9. little / **b**ig / small

To solve the riddle, write the bold letters in order on the lines below.

What kind of bulb does not need water?

__ __ __ __ __ __ __ __ __

Word Games: Grades 1–2

Name _____

United Together

The United Nations is a group of countries that work together for world peace and a better way of life for all people. October 24 is United Nations Day.

Make new words by using the letters in **United Nations**. Use the Word Bank to help you fill in the blanks.

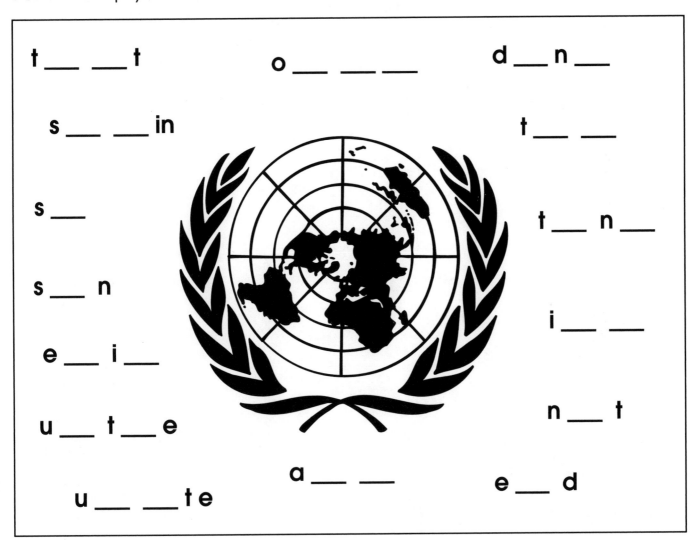

t __ __ t   o __ __ __   d __ n __

s __ __ in   t __ __

s __   t __ n __

s __ n   i __ __

e __ i __

u __ t __ e   n __ t

u __ __ t e   a __ __   e __ d

Word Bank

tent	dent	so	inn	ten
untie	tune	ant	end	nut
satin	son	edit	oats	unite

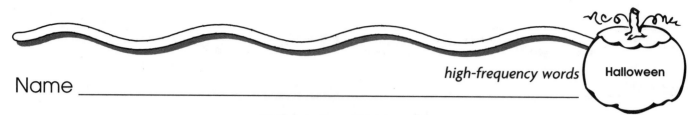

Name _____

Candy Treats

Fill your bag with candy by solving the puzzle below.

Use the Word Bank to find the words that go together like "salt and pepper."

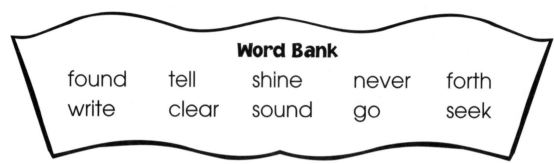

Word Bank

found	tell	shine	never	forth
write	clear	sound	go	seek

1. Jack found his coat in the lost and __ ◯ __ __ __.

2. The traffic was stop-and-◯__.

3. Maria's favorite game is hide-and-__ __ __ __.

4. I can hear you loud and __ ◯ __ __ __.

5. Jon learned to read and __ __ ◯ __ __.

6. Today is show-and- __ __ __ __.

7. It is time to rise and __ __ __ __ __.

8. It is now or __ ◯ __ __ __.

9. The puppy was safe and __ __ ◯ __ __.

10. The ball bounced back and __ __ __ __ ◯.

To solve the riddle, write each circled letter in the blank above the correct number.

What position does a monster play on a soccer team?

___ ___ ___ ___ ___ ___ ___
 2   10   1   9   4   5   8

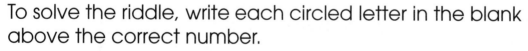

Name _____

Corn-Popping Treats

Corn is one of the most important crops grown in the United States. When you heat a kernel of corn, it will pop. Then you have popcorn! October is National Popcorn Popping Month.

Use the letters in the pieces of popcorn to make words on each word family bag.

Name _____

"Dino" Might

Dinosaurs are giant reptiles that lived millions of years ago.

Unscramble each word in the dinosaur eggs by writing the syllables in the correct order on the blanks in the puzzle.

1. tile rep

2. od per i

3. ant gi

4. est larg

5. ssil fo

6. ions mill

7. i terr ble

8. ry his to

9. ture crea

10. co dis ve ry

1. _ _ _ _ _ _ _

2. _ _ _ _ _ _ _

3. _ _ _ _ _ _

4. _ _ _ _ _ _

5. _ _ _ _ _ _

6. _ _ _ _ _ _ _

7. _ _ _ _ _ _ _ _

8. _ _ _ _ _ _ _

9. _ _ _ _ _ _ _

10. _ _ _ _ _ _ _ _ _

What would you get if you crossed a pigeon, a frog, and a prehistoric monster? Hint: The answer is in the puzzle above.

a _ _ _ _ _ _ _ _ - _ _ _ _ dinosaur

Name _____

Counting Votes

Election Day is the first Tuesday after the first Monday in November. This is when we vote for people to run our government.

Read the clues given by each student to see who has the most votes for class president. Below each student, write the number word that tells how many votes that student received.

I have six fewer votes than Tara.

The number of votes I received is an even number between six and ten.

I have three fewer votes than Amy.

I have two more votes than Amy.

I have five more votes than Sam.

Sam

Tara

Amy

Ty

Josh

Circle the student with the most votes.

Name _____

May I Have a Sandwich, Please?

Sandwich Day is observed in November. To celebrate, let's make some super sandwiches.

Make each sandwich by starting with the word at the bottom. Remove the letter that is on each slice of bread. Use the remaining letters to make a new word.

t
e
h
c
teach

t
s
p
l
plants

t
s
e
d
tides

h
s
t
n
hints

Name _____

Where Would You Go?

The United States is made up of 50 states.

Use the Word Bank to solve each riddle.

Word Bank

Pennsylvania   Oregon

Washington   Montana

Tennessee   New Hampshire

1. What state would you go to if you had a huge pile of dirty clothes?

   _ _ _ _ _ _ _ _ _ _ _

2. What state would you go to if you needed a dime?

   _ _ _ _ _ _ _

3. What state would you go to if you wanted to lie out in the sun?

   _ _ _ _ _ _

4. What state would you go to if you wanted to write a letter?

   _ _ _ _ _ _ _ _ _ _ _ _

5. What state would you go to if you were a miner?

   _ _ _ _ _ _ _

6. What state would you go to if you wanted a sandwich?

   _ _ _ _ _ _ _ _ _ _ _ _

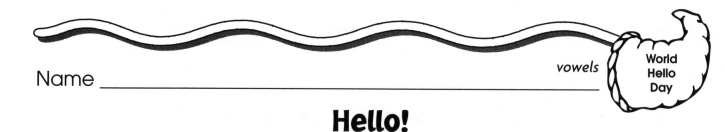

Name _____

Hello!

World Hello Day is celebrated in November. Saying hello is a nice way to be friendly to others.

Use the Word Bank to fill in the blanks with vowels to learn how to say hello in eight different languages. Then, circle each word in the puzzle. The words will go across and down.

Hello!

Ni Hao!

s	m	a	l	l	g	u	t	e	n
a	b	o	n	q	o	u	r	a	h
s	a	w	a	t	d	e	e	k	a
h	l	l	l	o	d	o	u	r	h
a	o	a	u	h	a	l	a	o	e
l	h	o	l	a	g	l	l	a	j
o	a	b	o	n	j	o	u	r	l
m	w	g	u	t	e	n	t	a	g

1. Swedish   g __ d d (__) g

2. Spanish   h __ (l)

3. Danish   h __ j

4. French   b __ n j (__) __ r

5. German   g __ t __ n t __ g

6. Hebrew   s(h)__ l __ m

7. Hawaiian   __ l __ h __

8. Thai   s __ w __ t d __ __ k (__) __

Word Bank
aloha
sawatdee kaa
guten tag
bonjour
shalom
hola
god dag
hej

To find out how to say good-bye in Hawaiian, write the circled letters in order on the blanks. __ __ __ __ __
                                    5   2   4   6   1

Word Games: Grades 1-2

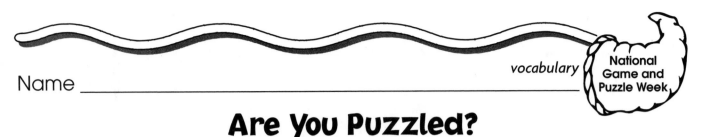

Name _____

Are You Puzzled?

Everyone loves the challenge of a puzzle. In celebration of National Game and Puzzle Week, solve each word box puzzle. A word box puzzle reads the same across as it does down.

Use the clues to complete the puzzles.

1. opposite of **yours**
2. something you think of
3. a report of an event
4. opposite of **west**

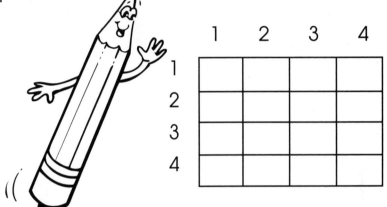

	1	2	3	4
1				
2				
3				
4				

	1	2	3	4
1				
2				
3				
4				

1. what to do at a red light
2. rhymes with **ape**
3. opposite of **close**
4. things you write with

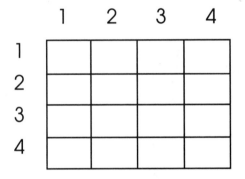

1. a fruit that rhymes with **mate**
2. open space
3. rhymes with **hens**
4. not hard

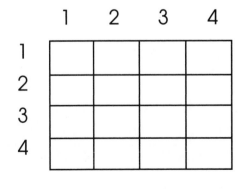

	1	2	3	4
1				
2				
3				
4				

Name _____

First Lion Exhibited in the U.S.

A Lion's Roar

A lion was first exhibited in America in Boston in 1716.

Unscramble each name of a zoo animal and write it in the puzzle. Use the Word Bank to help. Then, write each shaded letter in order to solve the riddle below.

Word Bank

penguin	panda	turtle
snake	toucan	goat
platypus	giraffe	bear

1. earb
2. danpa
3. ucanto
4. ffeagir
5. atypsupl
6. pgennui
7. ttlure
8. kaesn
9. tago

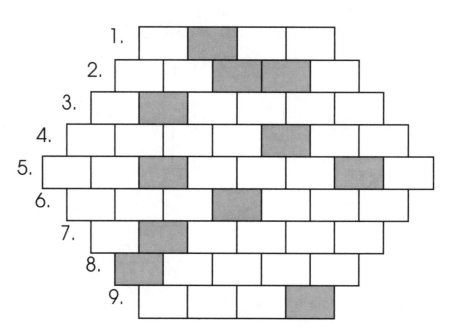

August was the name of a monkey who was always picking on larger animals. One day, he got into an argument with a lion. The next day was the first of September. Why?

It was the __ __ __   __ __ __ __ __ __ __ __ __ __!

Name _____

Strutting Turkey

Thanksgiving is celebrated in the U.S. on the fourth Thursday in November. It is a time to share and give thanks for the things one has.

Color each feather red if the word makes the **short a** sound as in **thank**.
Color each feather yellow if the word makes the **long a** sound as in **ate**.
Color each feather purple if the word makes the **short u** sound as in **cut**.
Color each feather orange if the word makes the **long u** sound as in **huge**.

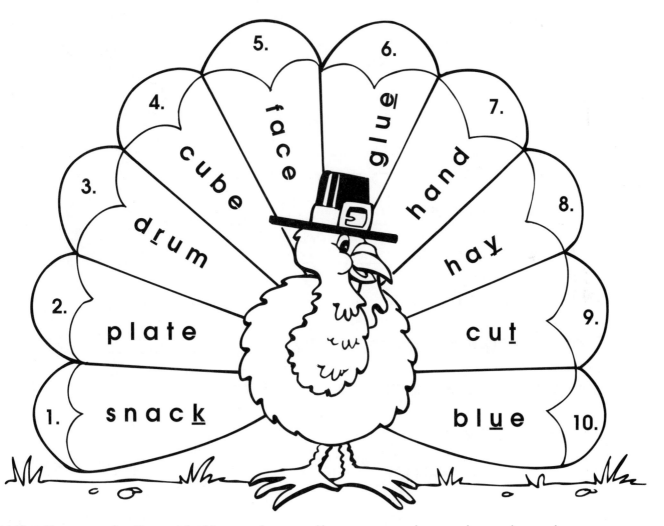

Write the underlined letters above the correct numbers to solve the riddle.

What kind of key will not open a door?   a __ __ __ __ __ __
                                               9 10 3 1 6 8

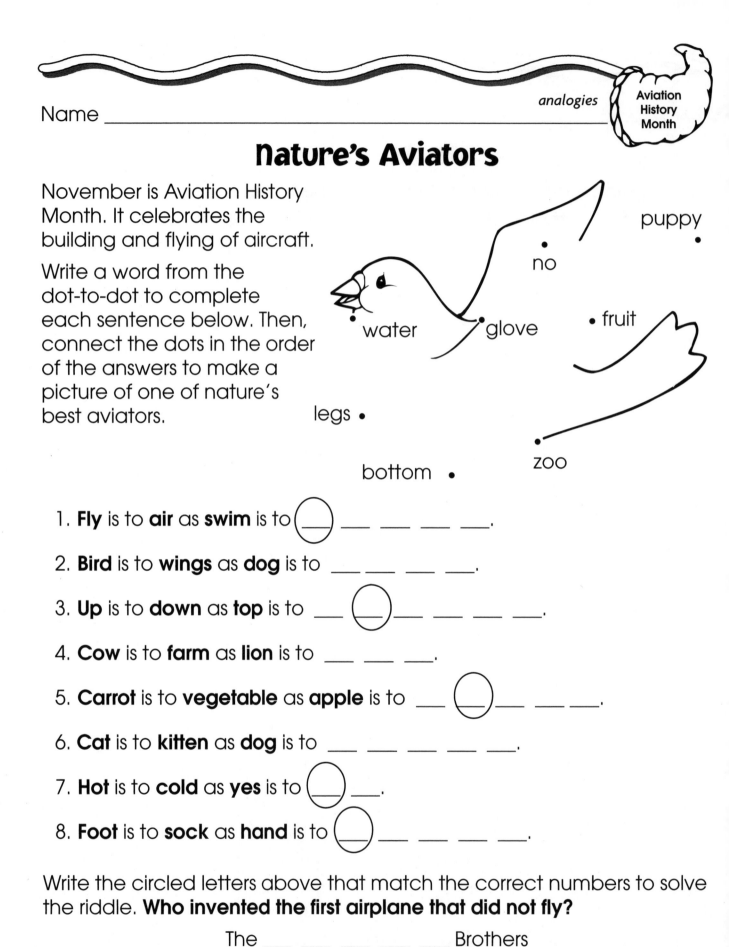

Name _____

Nature's Aviators

November is Aviation History Month. It celebrates the building and flying of aircraft.

Write a word from the dot-to-dot to complete each sentence below. Then, connect the dots in the order of the answers to make a picture of one of nature's best aviators.

puppy

no

water glove fruit

legs

zoo

bottom

1. **Fly** is to **air** as **swim** is to (__) __ __ __ __ .

2. **Bird** is to **wings** as **dog** is to __ __ __ __ .

3. **Up** is to **down** as **top** is to __ (__) __ __ __ __ .

4. **Cow** is to **farm** as **lion** is to __ __ __ .

5. **Carrot** is to **vegetable** as **apple** is to __ (__) __ __ __ .

6. **Cat** is to **kitten** as **dog** is to __ __ __ __ __ .

7. **Hot** is to **cold** as **yes** is to (__) __ .

8. **Foot** is to **sock** as **hand** is to (__) __ __ __ __ .

Write the circled letters above that match the correct numbers to solve the riddle. **Who invented the first airplane that did not fly?**

The __ __ __ __ __ Brothers
     1   5   3   7   8

Brightest Star

On December 3, 1621, Galileo perfected the telescope. A telescope magnifies distant objects. It is used to study planets like Mars and stars like Sirius. Sirius is the brightest star.

Color each star yellow if it contains a word with the same vowel sound as in **star**.

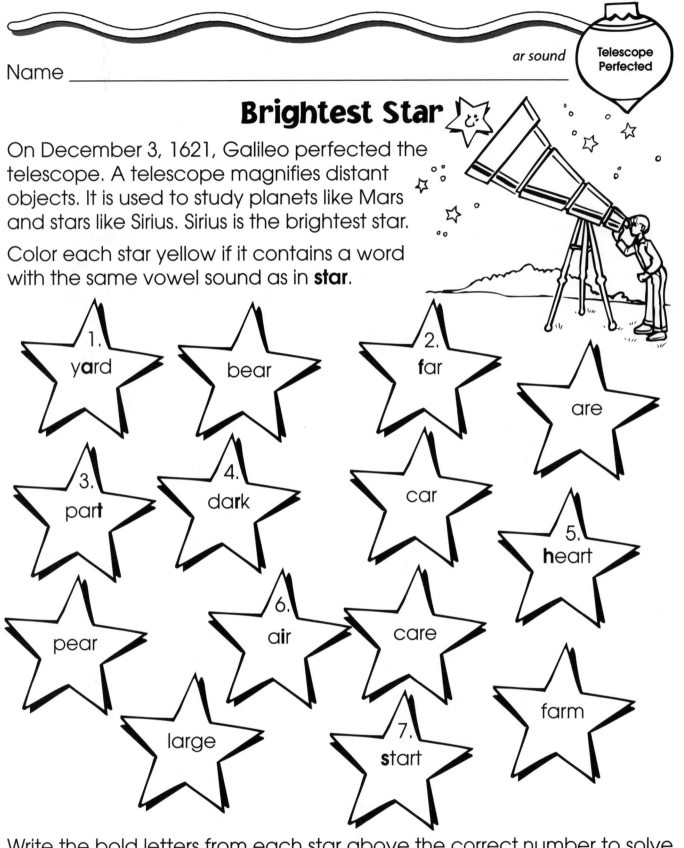

1. y**ar**d

bear

2. f**ar**

are

3. p**ar**t

4. d**ar**k

car

5. h**eart**

pear

6. air

care

farm

large

7. st**ar**t

Write the bold letters from each star above the correct number to solve the riddle. **What kind of fish did the astronaut see?**

___ ___ ___ ___ ___ ___ ___ ___ ___!
1   7   3   1   4   2   6   7   5

Name _____

Wonderful World of Disney

Walt Disney was born on December 5, 1901. He was one of the most famous movie producers in history.

Read the clues to find out some of Walt Disney's favorite characters. Write the number of the character next to its clue. Then, circle each character in the puzzle. The words will go across and down.

S	N	O	A	P	S	E	M	S
C	O	P	R	O	I	K	I	I
A	W	A	I	C	M	U	C	M
M	I	S	T	A	R	Z	A	N
P	D	I	I	H	D	C	M	D
D	U	M	B	O	U	O	I	B
O	C	B	K	N	C	A	C	E
C	K	A	U	T	B	R	K	L
K	U	P	Z	A	R	I	E	L
A	D	A	I	S	Y	T	Y	E

____ the name of a mouse

____ a famous duck

____ a boy who was raised by a gorilla

____ a lion who could not wait to be king

____ a daughter of a chief

____ an emperor who was turned into a llama

____ the littlest mermaid who married Eric

____ a baby elephant with big ears

____ a beauty that fell in love with a beast

____ the son of Lady and Tramp

Word Bank

1. SCAMP
2. BELLE
3. KUZCO
4. MICKEY
5. DAISY
6. TARZAN
7. SIMBA
8. POCAHONTAS
9. DUMBO
10. ARIEL

Walks with a Waddle

When the South Pole was discovered on December 14, 1911, penguins were found. Penguins cannot fly, but they are great swimmers. Penguins have very short legs and walk with a waddle.

Use the clues to write the words in the puzzle that end with **le** as in **waddle**. Then, write the letters in each shaded box in order to finish the sentence below.

Word Bank

needle	bottle	people
turtle	kettle	single
rattle	simple	double

1. baby's toy

2. something a baby drinks from

3. two of the same

4. something you boil water in

5. a group of men and women

6. a reptile with a shell

7. one

8. something you sew with

9. easy

Penguins build their nests and raise their young in huge colonies called

___ ___ ___ ___ ___ ___ ___ ___ ___.

Name _____

Tea Party

The Boston Tea Party was a raid by American colonists who dressed up like Native Americans and threw 342 chests of tea into the Boston Harbor to avoid being taxed.

Color the chest brown if you add **s** to make the word plural.

Color the chest yellow if you add **es** to make the word plural.

Color the chest green if you have to change the **y** to **i** and add **es** to make the word plural.

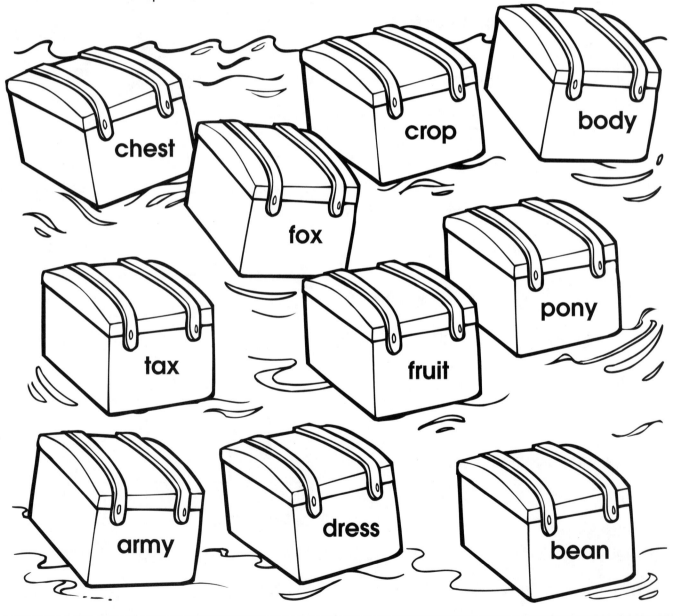

Name _____

Short Stack

Potato latkes are a traditional Hanukkah food. These pancakes are fried in oil. The oil is a reminder of the Hanukkah miracle.

Write the word from the Word Bank that is the last part of one compound word and the first part of another compound word.

Word Bank

ball   book   fly   fish   bee   man   light   yard   down

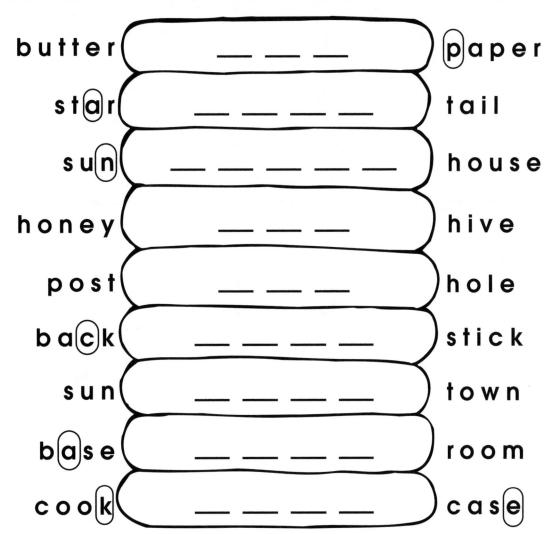

butter ___ ___ ___ paper

star ___ ___ ___ ___ tail

sun ___ ___ ___ ___ ___ house

honey ___ ___ ___ hive

post ___ ___ ___ hole

back ___ ___ ___ ___ stick

sun ___ ___ ___ ___ town

base ___ ___ ___ ___ room

cook ___ ___ ___ ___ case

Write each circled letter in order on the blanks to solve the riddle.

What kind of cake do you eat for breakfast? ___ ___ ___ ___ ___ ___ ___

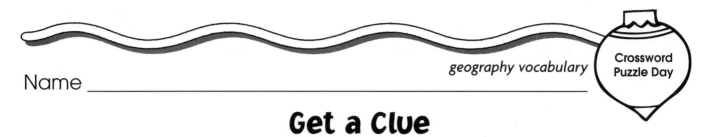

Crossword Puzzle Day

Name _____

Get a Clue

The first crossword puzzle appeared in the *New York World* newspaper on December 21, 1913.

Match the shape of each state to write its name in the puzzle.

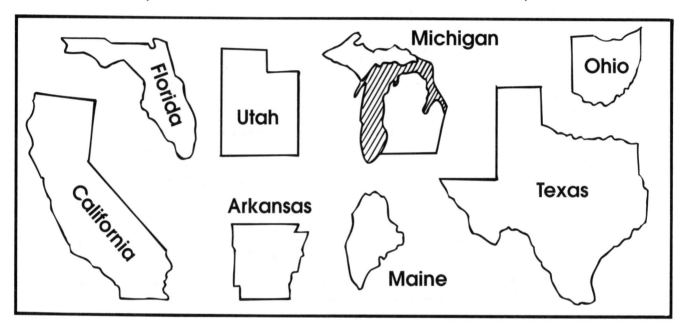

Across

Down

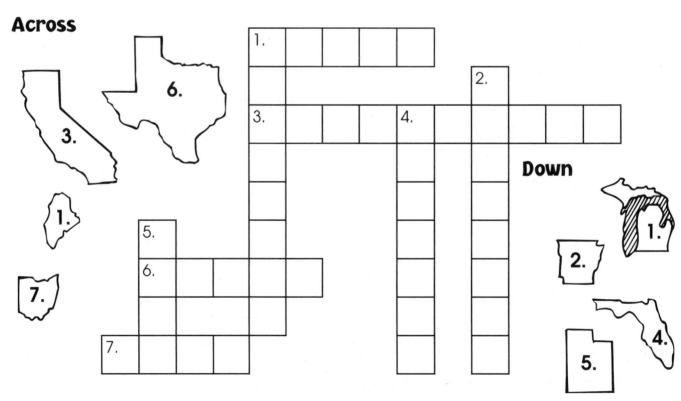

Name _____

Hung with Care

Some children hang stockings on their fireplaces in hopes that Saint Nicholas will come and fill them with toys.

1. Draw a brightly colored beach ball on the first, fourth, sixth, and ninth stockings.

2. Draw a candy cane on the second, fifth, and tenth stockings.

3. Draw a star on the third, seventh and eighth stockings.

4. Write a girl's name and draw red stripes on the stockings that follow the first, third, sixth, and eighth stockings.

5. Write a boy's name and draw green stripes on the first, third, sixth, eighth, and tenth stockings.

6. What stocking does not have a name on it? ___ ___ ___ ___ ___
Write your name on that stocking.

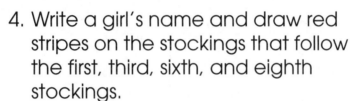
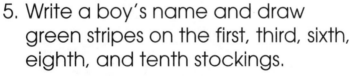

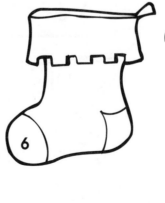

Name _____

Let's Make a Mkeka!

Kwanzaa is an African-American holiday that begins December 26. It celebrates the African festival of the harvest of the first crop. Kwanzaa means "first fruits" in Swahili. Mkeka means place mat.

Color each space red if the word is a fruit.

Color each space green if the word is a vegetable.

Color each space black if the word is neither.

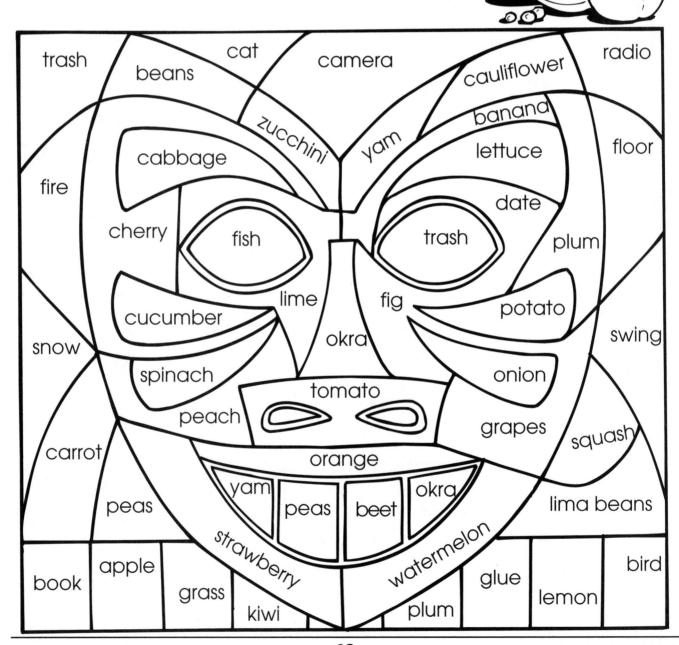

Name _____

One Nation

The Pledge of Allegiance was recognized on December 28, 1945. It was recommended that all schoolchildren should recite it every day before starting school.

Use the code to solve the puzzle.

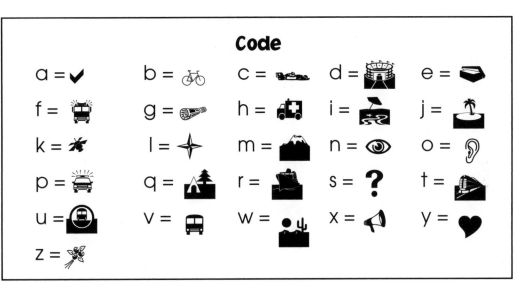

New Year's Day

Happy New Year!

January 1 is the beginning of a new year. It is called New Year's Day.

Write the correct number word in each blank. Then, use the letters on the calendar to solve the riddle below.

January

Sun.	Mon.	Tues.	Wed.	Thurs.	Fri.	Sat.
			a one	b two	c _____	d four
e _____	f six	g seven	h _____	i nine	j _____	k eleven
l twelve	m _____	n fourteen	o _____	p _____	q seventeen	r _____
s nineteen	t _____	u twenty-one	v _____-_____	w twenty-three	x _____-_____	y _____-_____
z twenty-six	_____-_____	_____-_____	twenty-nine	thirty	_____-_____	

What does a caterpillar do on New Year's Day?

_____ _____ _____ _____ _____   _____ _____ _____ _____   _____
20   21   18   14   19   15   22   5   18   1

_____ _____ _____   _____ _____ _____ _____ !
14   5   23   12   5   1   6

40

Name _____

National Clean Off Your Desk Day

Clean That Messy Desk!

Everyone likes to get organized to start the year off right. The second Monday in January is National Clean Off Your Desk Day.

Unscramble the letters of the names of things you might have on your desk. Write the words in the correct boxes below.

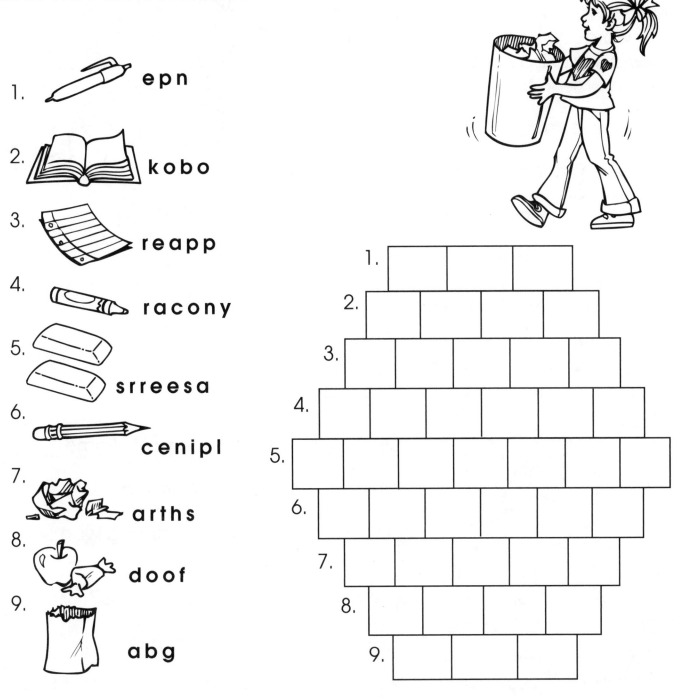

1. **e p n**

2. **k o b o**

3. **r e a p p**

4. **r a c o n y**

5. **s r r e e s a**

6. **c e n i p l**

7. **a r t h s**

8. **d o o f**

9. **a b g**

© Carson-Dellosa CD-4330

41

Word Games: Grades 1-2

A Hug a Day

January 21 is National Hug Day. The best way to celebrate this day is to hug your mom and dad or someone special to you.

Mom and Dad are palindromes. They are words spelled exactly the same, forward and backward. Circle each palindrome in the sentences.

1. Sis loves hugs, too.

2. Give a hug to the baby pup.

3. Give three people a hug at noon.

4. Lil had a bear hug on her bib.

5. Sam hugged the puppy named Otto.

6. Bob did a good deed and got a hug.

7. Dad hugged the kayak so he would not fall off.

Circle the phrases that are palindrome.

1. Jessica's hug earned the top spot.

2. The race car named Bear-Hug won.

Can you figure out the palindrome?

no __ __ __ __ __ , no melon

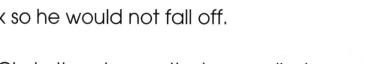

Are You Sick?

National School Nurse Day is January 23. It is a time to appreciate our nurses at school. They take care of us when we feel sick.

Color each tongue depressor red if it makes a word when you add **ick**.

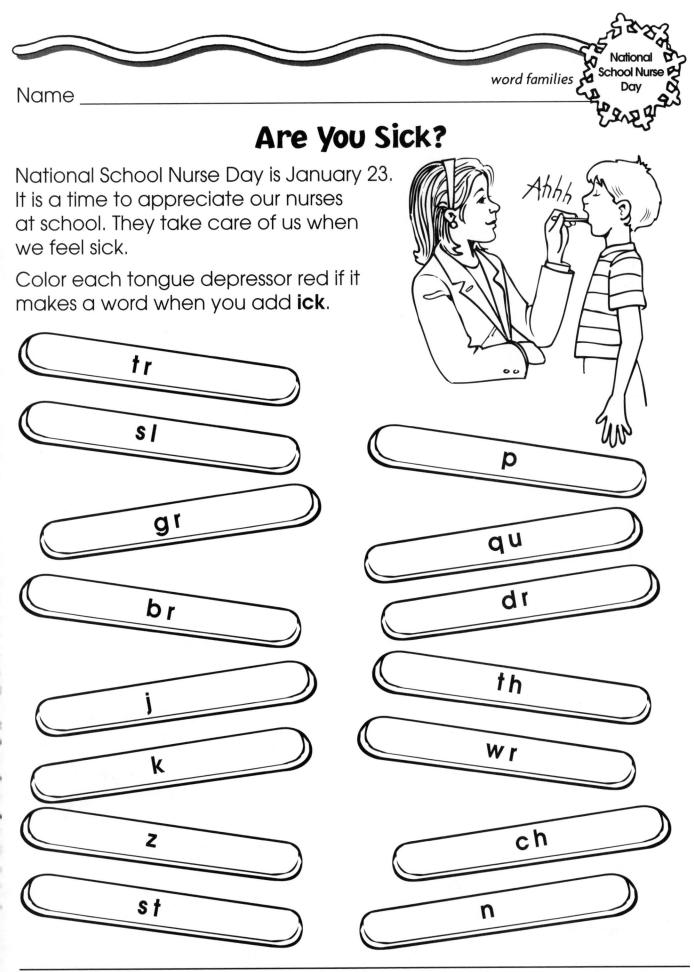

National School Nurse Day

Ahhh

t r

s l

g r

b r

j

k

z

s t

p

q u

d r

t h

w r

c h

n

Name _____

Gold Rush

Throughout history, people have wanted to strike it rich. On January 24, 1848, gold was discovered in California.

Discover more about money by using the Word Bank to complete the puzzle.

Word Bank

ten	cent	nickel	dollar
quarter	one	five	penny
dime	coins	twenty	

Down

1. Eight quarters and three one-dollar bills are equal to one _____ -dollar bill.

2. Paper money is called _____ bills.

3. 1¢

5. ¢

7. Dimes, nickels, pennies, and quarters are called _____.

9. Two five-dollar bills are equal to one _____-dollar bill.

Across

2. 10¢

4. 25¢

6. 5¢

8. two ten-dollar bills

10. Four quarters equal ___ dollar.

Name _____

Let's Make Music!

Mozart Week is the last week in January. Mozart was one of the greatest and most creative musical composers in history. Mozart was composing music at the age of five!

Color each space yellow if the word names a musical instrument. Color all the other spaces blue.

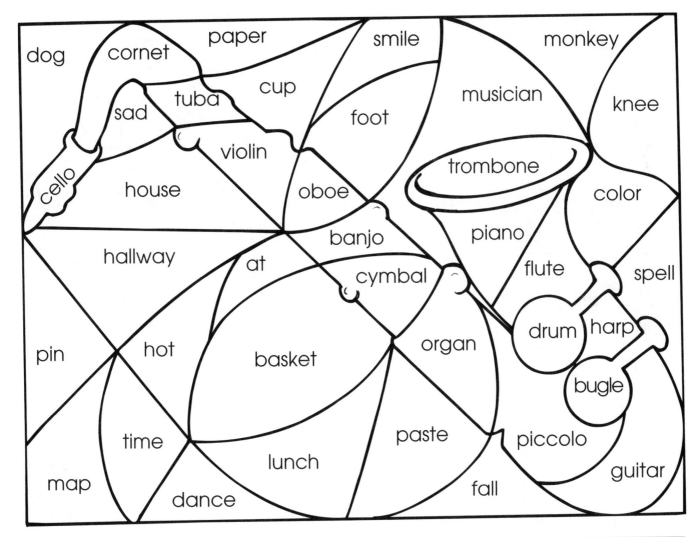

dog · cornet · paper · smile · monkey · tuba · cup · musician · knee · sad · foot · violin · trombone · color · cello · house · oboe · piano · banjo · flute · spell · hallway · at · cymbal · drum · harp · pin · hot · basket · organ · bugle · time · paste · piccolo · lunch · guitar · map · dance · fall

Use the code to solve the riddle.

What kind of phone makes music?

a __ __ __ __ __ __ __ __ __

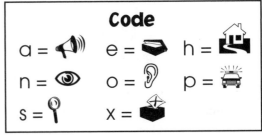

Code

a = 📢   e = 📇   h = 🏠
n = 👁   o = 👂   p = 🚓
s = 🔍   x = 📦

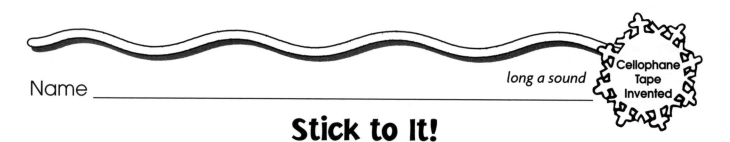

Cellophane
Tape
Invented

Name _____

Stick to It!

On January 31, 1928, cellophane tape was invented. This great invention has made our lives easier because it can hold many things together. How else could you wrap a present?

Solve the rebus puzzle with words with the **long a** sound as in **tape**. Stick to it!

1.  _ _ _ _ _ _ _

2. b + 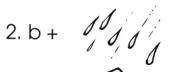 _ _ _ _ _

3. sp +  _ _ _ _ _

4.  _ _ _ _ _ _ _

5.  +  _ _ _ _ _ _

6. gr + 8 _ _ _ _ _

7.  _ _ _ _ _

8. + ache _ _ _ _ _ _

9. gr +  _ _ _ _ _

10. + ade _ _ _ _ _ _ _ _

Name _____

Um, Good!

January is National Soup Month. When it is cold outside, it feels good to eat something hot to keep warm inside.

Use the clues and the sound of each letter to write a word from the Word Bank.

Word Bank

tepee	peel	bee
empty	pea	easy
seal	buy	see
while	you	deal

1. not hard   EZ   __ __ __ __

2. water animal   CL   __ __ __ __

3. banana's skin PL   __ __ __ __

4. period of time YL   __ __ __ __

5. vegetable   P   __ __ __

6. kind of insect B   __ __ __

7. pass out cards DL   __ __ __ __

8. kind of tent   TP   __ __ __ __ __

9. to look   C   __ __ __

10. pronoun   U   __ __ __

11. to purchase   BI   __ __ __

12. not full   MT   __ __ __ __ __

Write the letters from the box in order to solve the riddle.

When do you swallow your words?

When you eat __ __ __ __ __ __   __ __ __ __ __!

Curl Up with a Good Book

January is National Book Month. It is a time for everyone to find a good book, curl up in a comfy spot, and read.

Circle the word in each worm section that rhymes with the top word. Then, solve the riddle by writing the circled letters in order on the blanks below.

sn(a)ck
take
tack

(b)ell
will
well

j(o)ke
woke
wore

cl(o)ck
stuck
stock

(w)ink
rink
ring

luc(k)
dunk
duck

bo(o)k
took
take

b(r)ight
ride
right

(m)ail
pail
pain

What kind of insect likes to read? __ __ __ __ __ __ __ __ __

Name _____

Chinese New Year

China's biggest celebration is Chinese New Year. It falls between January 21 and February 19. This holiday is celebrated with parades, fireworks, and traditional family meals. Each new year has an animal that represents that year.

Circle the word that has the same vowel sound as each animal in the Chinese zodiac.

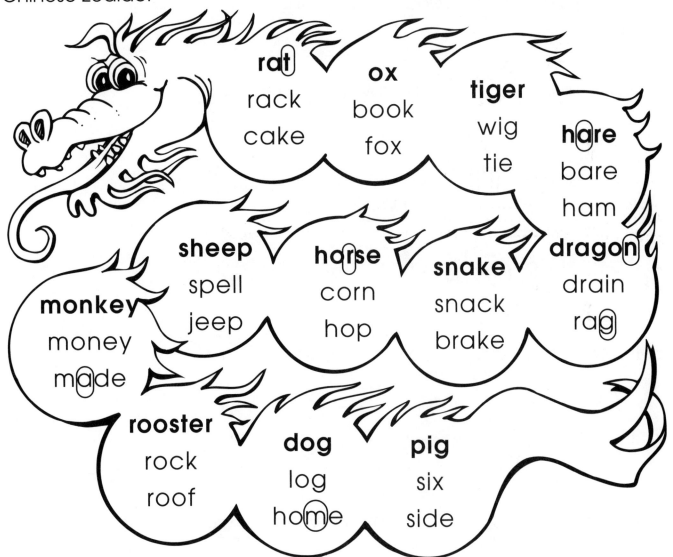

rat
rack
cake

ox
book
fox

tiger
wig
tie

hare
bare
ham

sheep
spell
jeep

horse
corn
hop

snake
snack
brake

dragon
drain
rag

monkey
money
made

rooster
rock
roof

dog
log
home

pig
six
side

To find out the name of an old Chinese puzzle, write the circled letters in order.

___ ___ ___ ___ ___ ___ ___

Name _____

Groundhog Day

According to tradition, a groundhog is awakened from its winter sleep on February 2. If the groundhog sees its shadow and goes back into its den, there will be six more weeks of winter.

Use the clues to find the names of other animals that sleep in the winter.

1. It begins like and rhymes with .

   _ _ _ _

2. It begins like and rhymes with  .

   _ _ _ _ _

3. It begins like and rhymes with  .

   _ _ _ _

4. It begins like and rhymes with .

   _ _ _

5. It begins like and rhymes with  .

   _ _ _ _

6. It begins like and rhymes with  .

   _ _ _ _ _

7. It begins like and rhymes with .

   _ _ _ _

g r o u n d h o g

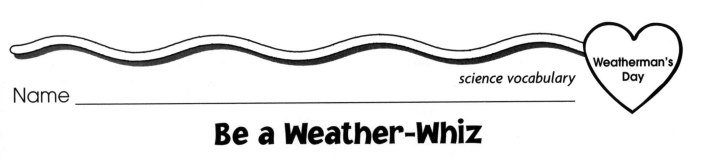

Name _____

Be a Weather-Whiz

February 5 is Weatherman's Day. Another name for weatherman is meteorologist, a person who forecasts and reports the weather.

Be a weather whiz and use each clue to solve the puzzle.

Word Bank			
wind	tornado	snow	clouds
rain	lightning	hail	rainbow

Across

3. a bow of colors in the sky
4. looks like marbles made of ice
6. small, white ice crystals
8. drops of water falling from the sky

Down

1. sometimes called a twister
2. tiny drops of water and specks of dust in the sky
5. electric spark during a storm
7. movement of air

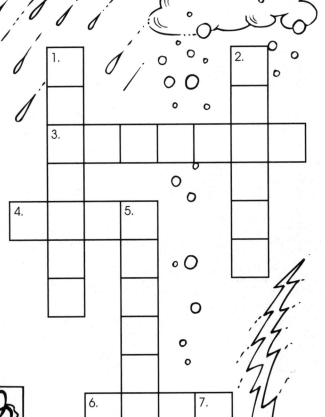

Name _____

Candy Hearts

February 14 is Valentine's Day. It is celebrated by giving cards and candy to someone special.

Color each heart red if the word on it has the **hard c** sound as in **candy**.

Color each heart pink if the word on it has the **soft c** sound as in **city**.

Write the circled letters in order to solve the riddle.

What did the postage stamp say to the envelope on Valentine's Day?

___ ___ ___ ___ ___ ___ ___ ___ ___ ___ ___!

Name _____

Amazing Astronaut

John Glenn orbited Earth three times in a space capsule on February 20, 1962. When the automatic controls failed, John Glenn had to take control of the capsule.

Take control and connect the dots in alphabetical order.

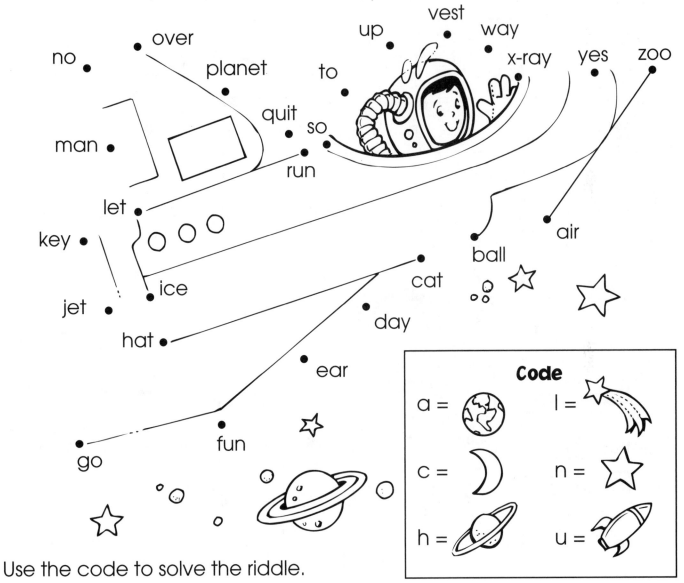

Use the code to solve the riddle.

Why did the astronaut blast off at noon?

It was time for ____ ____ ____ ____ ____ ____.

Name _____

Presidents' Day

Presidents' Day is the third Monday in February. This day is set aside to observe the birthdays of Abraham Lincoln (February 12) and George Washington (February 22).

Use the clues to find out which president's portrait is on each bill.

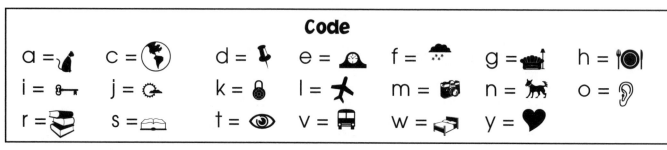

1. $2

2. $50

3. $20

4. $5

5. $500

6. $1,000

7. $5,000

8. $1

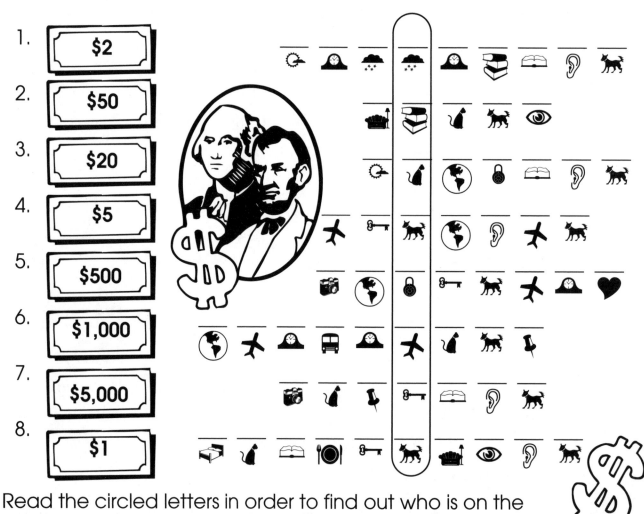

Read the circled letters in order to find out who is on the ten-dollar bill.

Famous African-Americans

In the month of February, famous African- Americans are celebrated. These people have contributed to America and have made this nation a better place.

Circle the last name of each political leader, athlete, and entertainer.

Circle the first name or initials of each writer, educator, scholar, and civil rights leader. Then, find each circled name or initials in the puzzle. They will go across and down.

Political Leaders

COLIN POWELL

L. DOUGLAS WILDER

CONDOLEEZZA RICE

Athletes

MAGIC JOHNSON

JACKIE ROBINSON

JACKIE JOYNER-KERSEE

Entertainers

OPRAH WINFREY

MILES DAVIS

DENZEL WASHINGTON

G	W	E	N	D	O	L	Y	N	B	J
O	O	D	R	J	R	A	S	W	O	O
M	P	A	I	O	I	B	M	A	R	Y
M	O	V	C	Y	C	W	O	S	O	N
A	W	I	N	L	E	E	Y	H	B	E
R	E	S	P	C	D	B	K	I	I	R
T	L	B	O	O	K	E	R	N	N	K
I	L	W	I	L	D	E	R	G	S	E
N	R	O	S	A	O	E	E	T	O	R
C	O	C	J	O	H	N	S	O	N	S
M	A	Y	A	J	O	H	N	N	S	E
W	I	N	F	R	E	Y	M	A	J	E

Writers, Educators, and Scholars

BOOKER T. WASHINGTON

MARY McLEOD BETHUNE

GWENDOLYN BROOKS

MAYA ANGELOU

Civil Rights Leaders

MARTIN LUTHER KING

ROSA LEE PARKS

W.E.B. DuBOIS

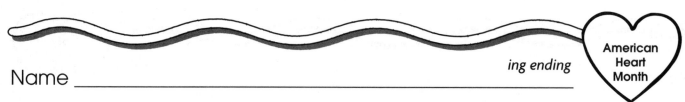

The Heart of the Matter

February is American Heart Month. Eating right and exercising are both good for your heart.

Color each space red that names things that make your heart beat faster. Color each space blue that names things that make your heart beat slower.

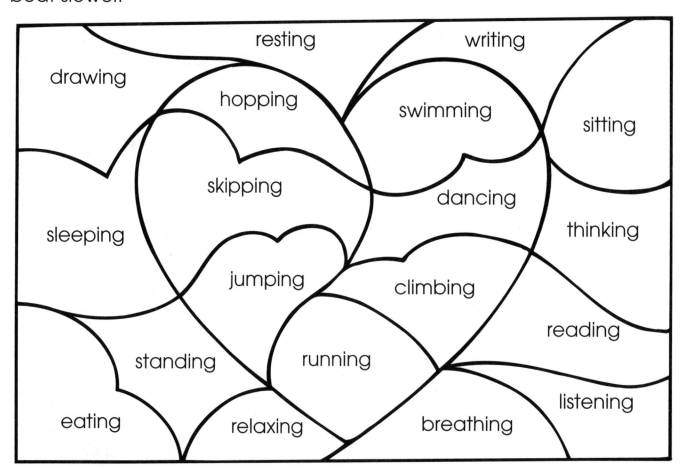

resting writing drawing hopping swimming sitting skipping dancing sleeping thinking jumping climbing standing running reading eating relaxing breathing listening

Use the code to complete the sentence below.

Code
c = ☁ e = 🌡 h = 🎆 i = ♪ m = 🐈 n = 🐀 t = ✎ u = 🛍

The heart pumps the entire body's blood supply through the body

every ____ ____ ____ ____ ____ ____.
        🐈   ♪   🐀   🛍   ✎   🌡

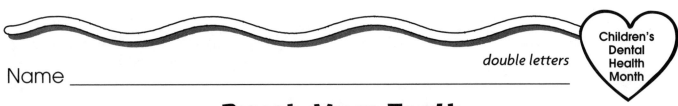

Children's
Dental
Health
Month

Name _____

Brush Your Teeth

You need your teeth to break up and chew food. Brushing your teeth and gums after meals and before bed helps keep them strong and healthy.

Several six-letter words contain double letters in the middle. Use the clues to help you complete each word.

1. hare

◯ __ bb __ __

2. something you hit a nail with

◯ __ mm __ __

3. laugh

__ ◯ gg __ __

4. nighttime meal

__ __ (n)n __ __

5. something you look into

__ __ rr ◯ __

6. something a dog wears

◯ __ ll __ __

7. a baby cat

__ __ tt ◯ __

8. opposite of winter

__ __ mm __ ◯

9. a color

__ __ ll ◯ __

10. opposite of rough

◯ __ oo __ __

Write the circled letters in order.

George Washington wore a set of false teeth made partly of

__ __ __ __ __ __ __ __ __ __ ivory.

Name _____

Oink! Oink!

On March 1, pigs are squealing all over the country. It is National Pig Day. Let's give all the pigs three big oinks. Oink! Oink! Oink!

Use the clues to solve the puzzle. All the words have the letters **ink** in them.

Word Bank

sink	blink	stinks
twinkle	sprinkle	wrinkle
drink	pink	shrink

1. opposite of float
2. to close and open your eyes
3. smells badly
4. something a star does
5. light rain
6. crease in the skin
7. to make smaller
8. to take a sip of
9. a color

1.
2.
3.
4.
5.
6.
7.
8.
9.

Write the letters in the shaded boxes in order to solve the riddle.

What telephone number does a pig call instead of nine-one-one when it gets into trouble?

__ __ __ __ __ -one-one

Dr. Seuss's Birthday

Name _____

Tip Your Hat to the Cat!

Dr. Seuss was born on March 2, 1904. He was the famous author of nearly 50 children's books, including *Hop on Pop* and *The Cat in the Hat*.

Circle the word that rhymes with the top word on each hat. Then, write a new word on the line below each hat that rhymes with the first word.

To find out what book Dr. Seuss wrote using fewer than 50 words, write the bold letters in order on the blanks below.

___ ___ ___ ___ ___   ___ ___ ___ ___ ___ ___

Name _____

Hello, Who Is This?

Alexander Graham Bell was born on March 3, 1847. He invented the telephone. On March 10, 1876, he said the first words that were transmitted by a telephone.

To find out what Bell said to his assistant, Thomas Watson, solve the puzzle using the letters on the telephone. Remember, for each number there is a choice of three letters.

" _C_ _ _M_ _ _ _H_ _ _E_ ,
   6   3   3   7

_W_ _ _ _S_ _ _N_ . _ _
 2   8   6   4

_ _ _E_ _ _D_ _ _ _O_ _ _ !"
6   3   9   8

Name _____

Size It Up!

Weights and measures are used to describe the amounts or sizes of things. Some of the first measurements were based on the human body. One foot originally was the length of a person's foot. Now it is 12 inches. One yard was the distance from the nose to the fingertip. Now it is three feet, or 36 inches.

Find the words on the measuring tools in the puzzle and circle them. The words will go across and down.

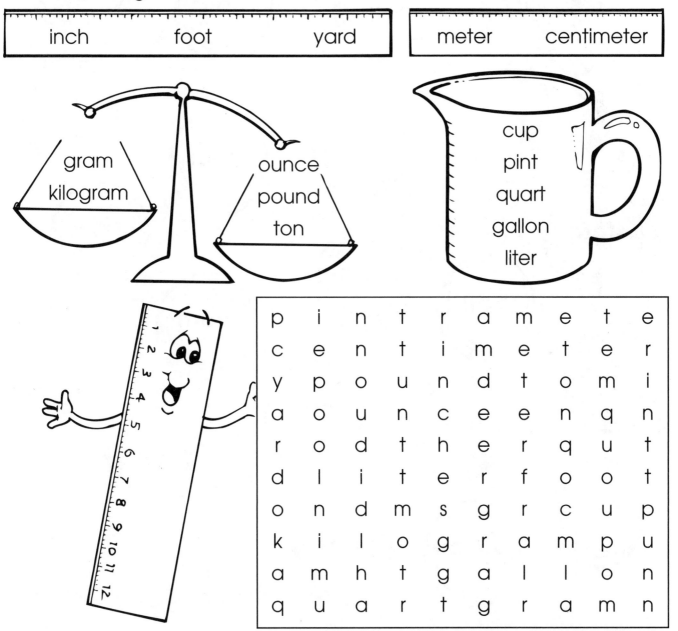

inch	foot	yard

meter	centimeter

gram
kilogram

ounce
pound
ton

cup
pint
quart
gallon
liter

p	i	n	t	r	a	m	e	t	e
c	e	n	t	i	m	e	t	e	r
y	p	o	u	n	d	t	o	m	i
a	o	u	n	c	e	e	n	q	n
r	o	d	t	h	e	r	q	u	t
d	l	i	t	e	r	f	o	o	t
o	n	d	m	s	g	r	c	u	p
k	i	l	o	g	r	a	m	p	u
a	m	h	t	g	a	l	l	o	n
q	u	a	r	t	g	r	a	m	n

Name _____

Pot of Gold Coins

St. Patrick's Day is celebrated on March 17. Legend has it that at the end of the rainbow, there is a pot of gold.

Help the leprechaun find his pot of gold by coloring each coin yellow if the word in it makes the **oi** sound as in **coin**.

vowels

International Day of the Seal

Seal Appeal

March 18 is the International Day of the Seal. On this day, everyone should enjoy seals and learn more about them. A seal is a very smart animal—smart enough to learn to balance a ball on its nose.

Write the missing vowel, **a**, **e**, **i**, **o**, or **u**, on each ball to make a word.

Make a list of five other words you could have made using a different vowel.

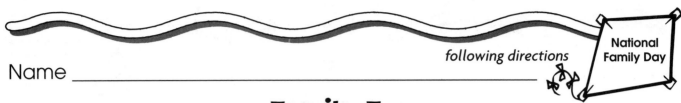

Name _____

Family Fun

National Family Day is March 25. It is a day when families should take time to do something fun together.

To find a fun family activity, follow the directions.

Color clothing words yellow.   Color food words blue.

Color toy words black.   Color furniture words red.

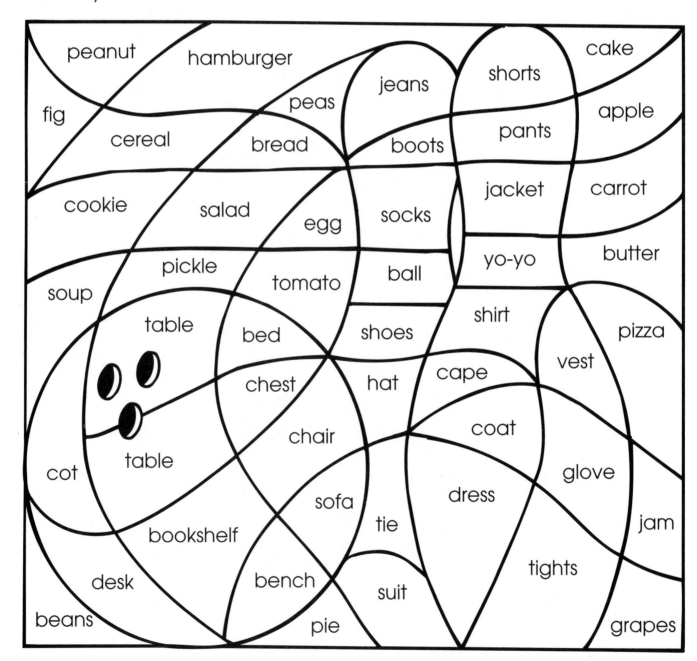

Name _____

We Are What We Eat!

Eating the right foods is important. To help people choose the right foods, the U.S. government developed a food pyramid.

Write each word from the Word Bank next to the correct space in the food pyramid.

Word Bank					
vegetables	fats	fruits	breads	dairy	meats

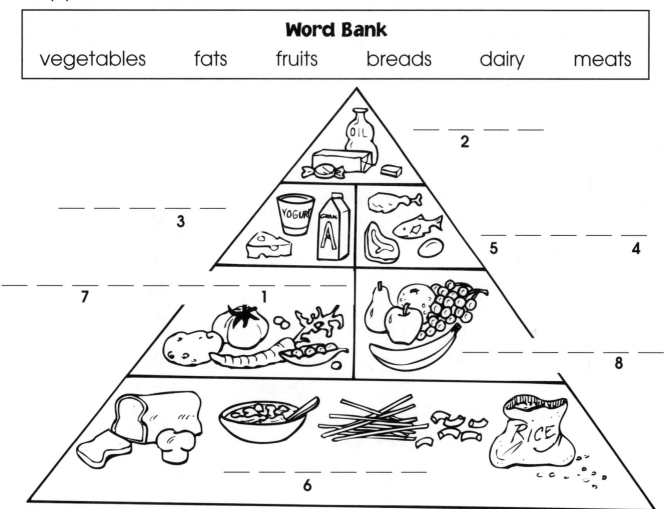

Write each numbered letter in the correct blank.

The foods at the bottom of the pyramid are the ones you should eat in

the __ __ __ __ __ __ __ amounts. At the top are the foods
    1 2 3 7 6 4 8

you should eat in the __ __ __ __ __ __ __ __ amounts.
          4 5 2 1 1 6 4 8

Easter

On Easter, many children like to go on Easter egg hunts.

Write each word from the Word Bank next to the correct clue. Then, to answer the riddle below, write the circled letters in order on the blanks.

1. goes well with peanut butter __ __ __ __ __ __
2. what chicks hatch from __ __ __ __
3. a candy flavor __ __ __ __ __
4. white puffy treat __ __ __ __ __ __ __ __ __ __ __
5. rhymes with sandy __ __ __ __ __
6. young rabbit __ __ __ __ __
7. something to hold things in __ __ __ __ __ __
8. green and grows in the ground __ __ __ __ __
9. a kind of hat __ __ __ __ __ __
10. baby chickens __ __ __ __ __ __

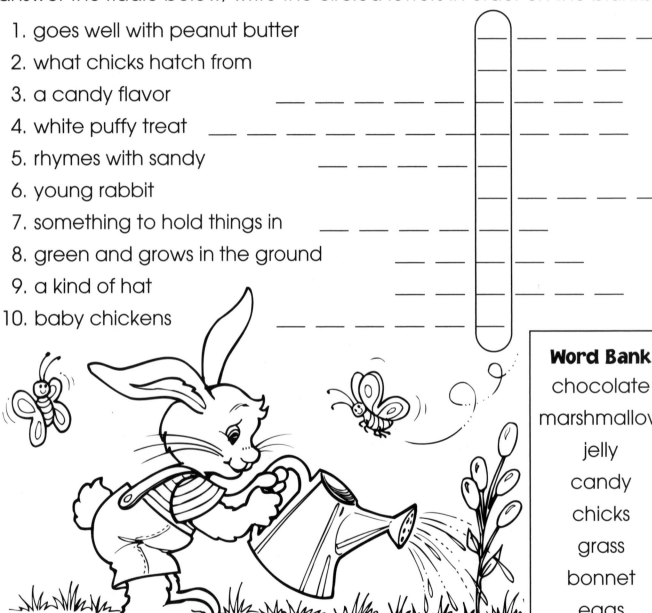

What does the Easter bunny plant in his garden?

__ __ __ __ __ __ __   __ __ __ __ __

Word Bank

chocolate
marshmallow
jelly
candy
chicks
grass
bonnet
eggs
basket
bunny

Name _____

Peter's Prank

It is April Fools' Day, and Peter celebrated by playing a prank on Mrs. Frank's class. Peter took all the fish out of the two fish tanks.

Help Peter put the fish back in the right tanks. Use the blend on each fish to make new words. If the fish makes a word by adding **ank,** color the fish green and write the word in the **ank** bowl. If the fish makes a word by adding **ake**, color the fish blue and write the word in the **ake** bowl.

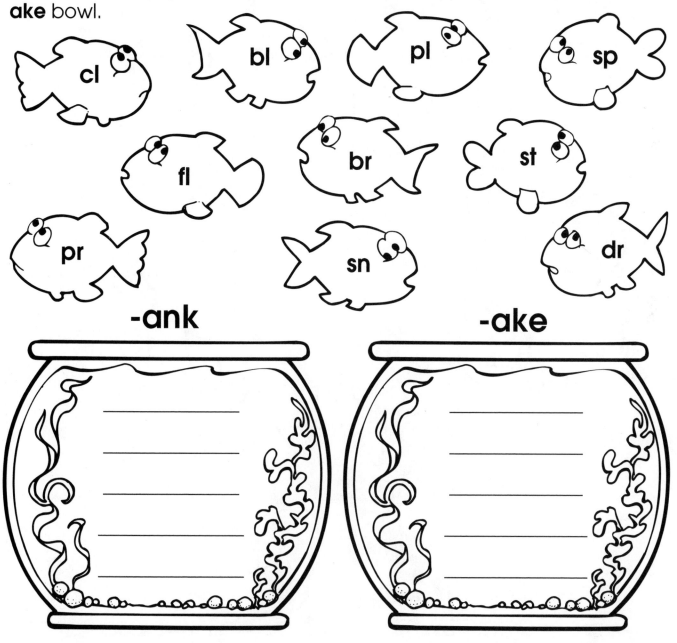

Arbor Day

Name _____

Plant a Tree

Arbor Day is celebrated in the spring. Often it is observed by planting a tree. A tree is home to many animals.

The letters on some of the acorns can make a new word by adding **unk**. See how many words you can make.

d

pl

cr

ch

sk

sn

bl

k

st

b

trunk

shr

j

HOME SWEET HOME

CHIPPY CHIPMUNK

Name _____

Ocean Animals

National Week of the Ocean is in April. The blue whale is the largest animal in the ocean. In fact, it is the largest animal in the world.

Circle each ocean animal from the Word Bank in the puzzle. To solve the riddle below, write a word going down in the puzzle.

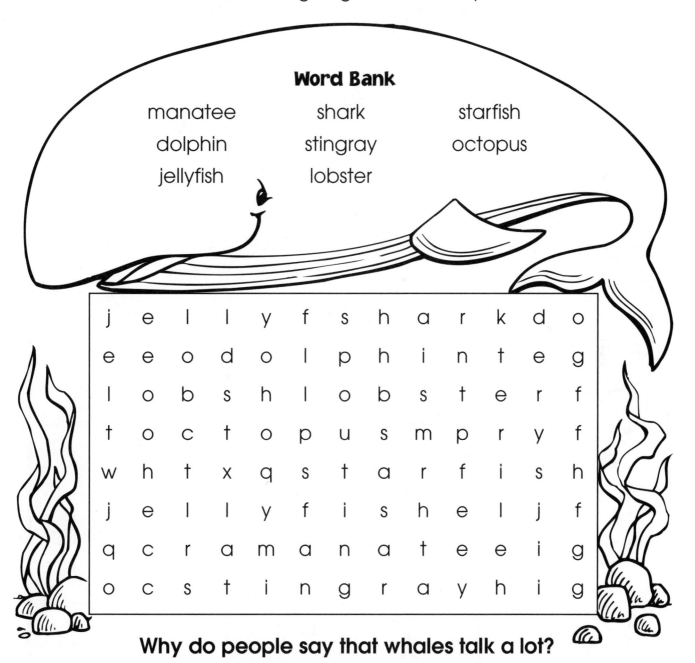

Word Bank

manatee	shark	starfish
dolphin	stingray	octopus
jellyfish	lobster	

j e l l y f s h a r k d o
e e o d o l p h i n t e g
l o b s h l o b s t e r f
t o c t o p u s m p r y f
w h t x q s t a r f i s h
j e l l y f i s h e l j f
q c r a m a n a t e e i g
o c s t i n g r a y h i g

Why do people say that whales talk a lot?

Because they are always __ __ __ __ __ __ __ __ off!

Name _____

Reduce, Reuse, and Recycle

Earth Day is April 22. Celebrate by recycling.

Write the things made with recycled materials in the puzzle.

Recycled Paper
newspaper
cereal boxes
wrapping paper
cardboard

Recycled Metal
cars
cans
nails
bicycles

Recycled Plastic
soda bottles
cameras
benches
shoes
carpeting

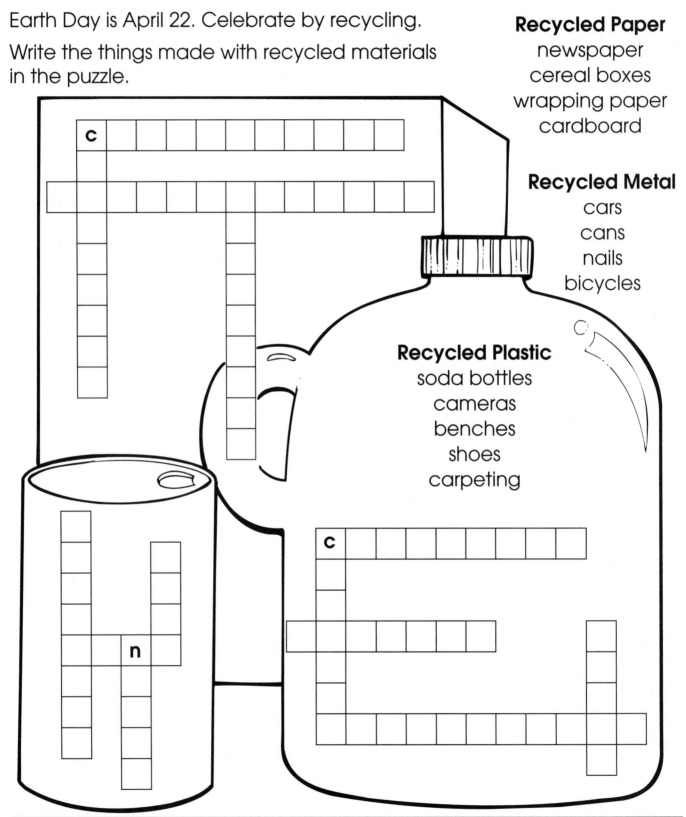

Name _____

Don't "Fowl" Up!

John James Audubon spent his life studying and painting pictures of birds. His birthday is April 26.

Some birds' names have smaller words in them. For example, the word **crow** has **row** in it. Write a word from the Word Bank to answer each question. Write the circled letters in order on the blanks at the bottom of the page to learn another bird fact.

Word Bank				
bluejay	**gold**finch	peli**can**	**rob**in	tur**key**
cardinal	**jack**daw	pheas**ant**	sand**piper**	

1. What bird has a boy's name in its name? __ __ Ⓞ __ __

2. What other bird has a boy's name in its name? __ Ⓞ __ __ __ __ __

3. What bird has a metal container in its name? __ __ Ⓞ __ __ __ __

4. What bird has a musician in its name? __ __ __ Ⓞ __ __ __ __ __

5. What bird can get into locked places? __ __ __ __ Ⓞ __

6. What bird has an automobile in its name? __ Ⓞ __ __ __ __ __ __

7. What bird is worth a lot? Ⓞ __ __ __ __ __ __ __ __

8. What bird has a color in its name? __ Ⓞ __ __ __ __ __

9. What bird has a tiny insect in its name? __ __ Ⓞ __ __ __ __

Our national bird is the __ __ __ __ __ __ __ __ __ __ __.

Name _____

Be Honest

National Honesty Day is April 30. Honesty means to tell the truth. An honest person is also sincere and keeps promises. An honest person does not steal, cheat, or behave in a tricky manner.

Write the contraction for each pair of underlined words.

Dad, I broke your new screwdriver.

1. An **h**onest pers**o**n <u>does **n**ot</u> ch**e**at. _____

2. <u>It **is**</u> important **t**o keep **y**our prom**is**es. _____

3. <u>She is</u> **t**ru**th**ful. _____

4. <u>We are</u> doing our **b**est to b**e** loyal. _____

5. <u>I will</u> alway**s** tell the **t**ruth. _____

6. <u>We will</u> **p**romise to be h**o**nest. _____

7. <u>You are</u> to always do the **r**ight thing. _____

8. **C**athy <u>does not</u> steal. _____

To find out a famous saying, write the bold letters in order on the blanks below.

___ ___ ___ ___ ___ ___ ___ ___ ___ ___   ___ ___ ___ ___ ___ ___ ___ ___ ___

___ ___ ___ ___ ___ ___ ___ ___ ___ ___ ___ ___ ___ ___ ___ ___ ___!

Name _____

It All Adds Up!

Math plays an important part in everyone's life. We use some kind of math skill every day. We use math to tell time and to buy things at the grocery store.

Use the clues to solve the crossword puzzle.

Across

1. eleven, thirteen, _____, seventeen

6. Twenty minus seven equals _____.

7. Two plus one equals _____.

8. Fifteen minus eight equals _____.

Down

1. Twelve plus two equals _____.

2. two, four, six, _____, ten

3. Three plus seven equals _____.

4. Six plus two plus four equals _____.

5. Ten minus three minus one equals _____.

6. five, ten, fifteen, _____, twenty-five

Name _____

Better Be Safe

April is National Youth Sports Safety Month. It is always important to follow the rules and be careful when playing sports or playing on a playground.

To find out one piece of sports equipment you should always wear when roller-skating, riding your bike, or hitting a baseball, follow the directions.

Color each word red that has another word hidden in it. The words **I** and **a** do not count. Color all other words blue.

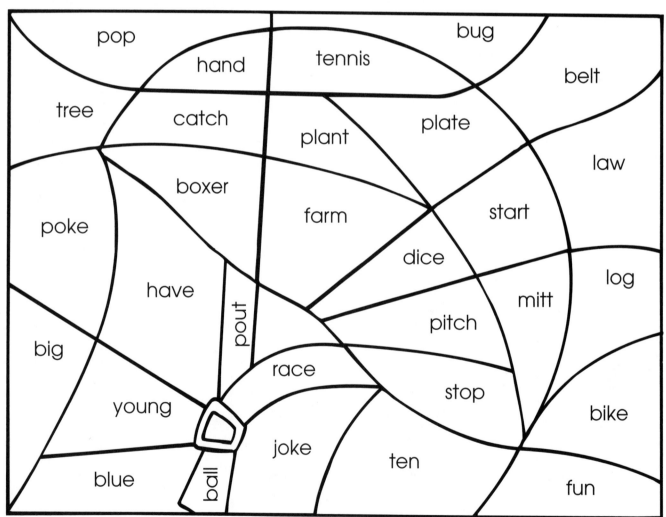

You should always wear a ___ ___ ___ ___ ___ ___.

What is one of the words hidden in it? ___ ___ ___

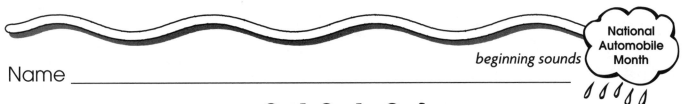

Name _____

Get Set, Go!

Every few seconds, a brand new car comes out of a car factory somewhere in the world.

To see which car comes off the assembly line first, color each block that makes a word when the beginning sound in the box is put before the word family on the car. The car that makes the most words is the winner!

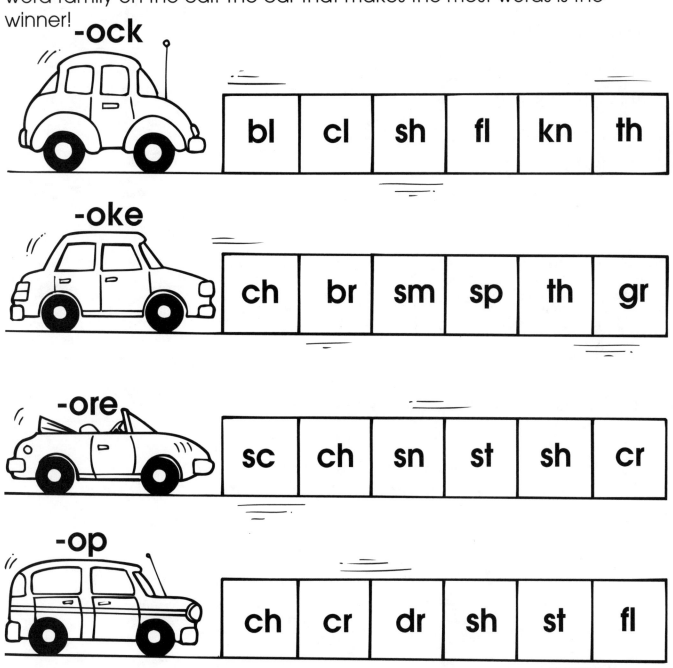

-ock

| bl | cl | sh | fl | kn | th |

-oke

| ch | br | sm | sp | th | gr |

-ore

| sc | ch | sn | st | sh | cr |

-op

| ch | cr | dr | sh | st | fl |

75

Word Games: Grades 1–2

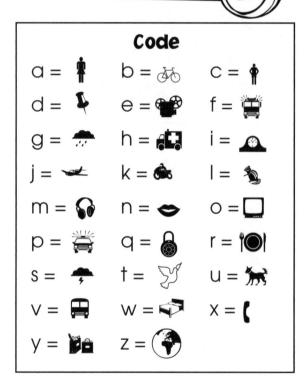

National Humor Month

Name _____

Grin and Giggle

Grab your funny bone because the month of April is National Humor Month.

Answer each question. Then, write each answer in order on the blanks below to solve the riddle.

1. the letter before **b** _____

2. the letter after **k** _____

3. the letter between **o** and **q** _____

4. the letter after **g** _____

5. the letter before **b** _____

6. the letter before **c** _____

7. the letter between **d** and **f** _____

8. the letter before **u** _____

9. the letter before **t** _____

10. the letter after **n** _____

11. the letter between **t** and **v** _____

12. the letter after **o** _____

Code

a = 🚶   b = 🚲   c = 🧍

d = 📌   e = 🎥   f = 🚒

g = 🌧   h = 🚑   i = 🕰

j = ✈   k = 🏍   l = 🐿

m = 🎧   n = 👄   o = 📺

p = 🚓   q = 🔒   r = 🍽

s = ⛈   t = 🕊   u = 🐕

v = 🚌   w = 🛏   x = ☎

y = 🛍   z = 🌍

What is abcdefghijklmnopqrstuvwxyz, slurp? Someone eating

—— —— —— —— —— —— —— —— —— —— —— ——

Use the code to solve the sentence that contains all 26 letters of the alphabet.

Name _____

May Flowers

April showers bring May flowers. Celebrate May Day on May 1 by planting beautiful flowers.

Write as many compound words as you can by using the words on the petals of both flowers.

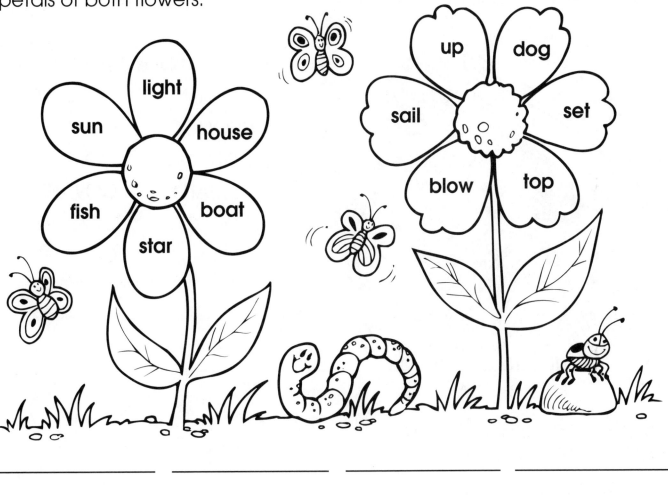

_____   _____

_____   _____

_____   _____

_____   _____

How did you do?

12 or more	**excellent**	7 to 11	**good**
4 to 6	**fair**	1 to 3	**Try again!**

It's a Celebration!

Cinco de Mayo is a Mexican holiday. It celebrates the victory of the Mexican Army over the French in the Battle of Puebla on May 5, 1862.

The English words in the Word Bank come from the Spanish language. Circle them in the puzzle. The words will go across and down.

Word Bank

BANANA	MUSTANG
BRONCO	COYOTE
CANYON	CORRAL
TOMATO	COWBOY
RODEO	COCOA
PATIO	CHILI

```
T  B  A  N  A  N  A  C  A  A
O  R  M  C  N  R  C  A  P  C
M  O  U  A  A  O  H  N  C  O
U  N  S  N  P  D  I  Y  O  C
S  C  T  Y  A  E  L  O  R  O
T  O  M  A  T  O  I  N  R  A
A  T  G  M  I  C  O  R  A  C
N  C  O  Y  O  T  E  O  L  O
G  C  O  W  B  O  Y  Y  P  A
```

National
Pet
Week

Name _____

Most Unusual Pets

Unusual pets are becoming more popular.

To find some of the most popular unusual pets, write the beginning letter for each picture word on the blanks.

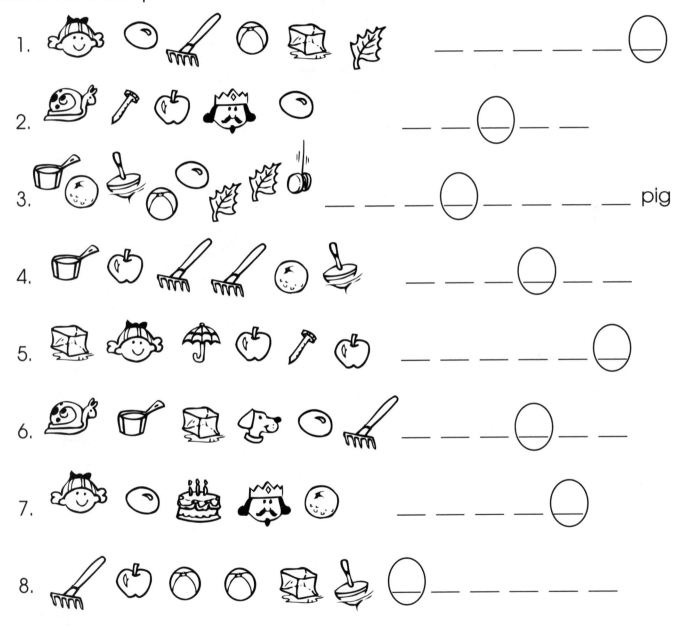

Name _____

Teacher's Gift

On Teachers' Day, Mrs. Lee's class decided to bring her gifts to show how much she is appreciated, but they forgot to label them.

Each gift rhymes with the name of the student who brought it. Use the Word Bank to write the correct name on each tag.

Word Bank

Jess	Ray	Matt	Kelly	Scott	Jake
Randall	Heather	Noelle	Ben	Blair	Dan

Happy Mother's Day

Our mothers are very special to us. We honor them on the second Sunday in May.

Use the Word Bank to solve each analogy.

Word Bank

children	eight	lost	mice	near	red
soft	south	teeth	two	won	

1. **Goose** is to **geese** as **mouse** is to _ _ _ _ .

2. **Sail** is to **sale** as **too** is to _ _ _ .

3. **Dark** is to **light** as **found** is to _ _ _ _ .

4. **Man** is to **men** as **child** is to _ _ _ _ _ _ _ _ .

5. **Wood** is to **would** as **read** is to _ _ _ .

6. **Fast** is to **slow** as **far** is to _ _ _ _ .

7. **Blew** is to **blue** as **ate** is to _ _ _ _ _ .

8. **East** is to **west** as **north** is to _ _ _ _ _ .

9. **Pare** is to **pear** as **one** is to _ _ _ .

10. **Happy** is to **sad** as **hard** is to _ _ _ _ .

11. **Foot** is to **feet** as **tooth** is to _ _ _ _ .

To find the name of one of the most famous mothers in literature, write the circled letters in order.

_ _ _ _ _ _ _ _ _

Name _____

All Kinds of Kites

Kites come in many different shapes. A delta kite has a triangular shape. A box kite consists of squares, rectangles, or triangles.

Use the clues to write the name of each shape in the puzzle.

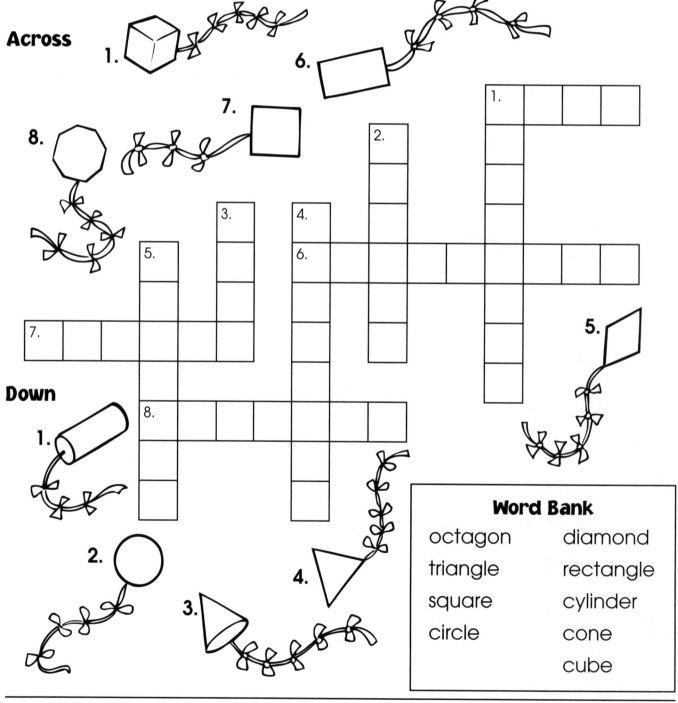

Across

Down

Word Bank

octagon	diamond
triangle	rectangle
square	cylinder
circle	cone
	cube

Name _____

A Climb to the Top!

The first team to climb Mt. Everest arrived at the top on May 29, 1953.

Climb to the top of each mountain by changing one letter of each word to make a new word. Start at the bottom.

cap

leg

_____ **g**

p _____

_____ **t**

m _____

ten

top

m _____

_____

b _____

far

p _____

_____

d _____

jog

Name _____

Memorial Day

Memorial Day is a day set aside to remember all who have died while serving our country. It is observed on the last Monday in May.

Answer each question using the words from the Word Bank.

Word Bank		
coast guard	marines	navy
military police	air force	army

1. soldiers who serve on land   ◯ __ __ __

2. soldiers who serve in the air

    __ __ __ ◯ __ __ __

3. soldiers who serve at sea   __ __ __ __

4. police that enforce laws in the military

__ __ __ __ __ __ __ __ __ __ ◯ __ __ __

5. soldiers who serve at sea, on land, and in the air

    __ ◯ __ __ __ __

6. people who protect our water borders

__ __ __ __ __ ◯ __ __ __ __

Write the circled letters in order to solve the riddle.

What rises in the morning and waves all day?

__ __ __ __ __

National Strawberry Month

Name _____

Favorite Fruit

A strawberry is a red, heart-shaped fruit. In most states, this delicious fruit is produced from May to November.

Unscramble the name of each fruit and circle it in the puzzle. The words will go across and down.

pplea

_ _ _ _ _

paergs

_ _ _ _ _ _

erpa

_ _ _ _

Inepppaie

_ _ _ _ _ _ _ _ _

aaannb

_ _ _ _ _ _

anergo

_ _ _ _ _ _

herrcy

_ _ _ _ _ _

mlie

_ _ _ _

p	a	o	r	b	a	n	a	n	c
i	p	g	r	a	p	e	s	o	h
n	p	r	a	n	a	p	p	p	e
p	i	n	e	a	p	p	l	e	r
l	i	m	e	n	p	e	a	a	r
e	p	i	n	a	l	p	e	r	y
o	r	a	n	g	e	a	r	s	p

Name _____

Father's Day

Father's Day is the third Sunday in June. Celebrate this day by doing something special with your dad. Hidden in the picture are some symbols of America's favorite pastime. It is something you could do with your dad.

Color each space brown if the word makes the **short a** sound as in **dad**. Color each space blue if the word makes the **long a** sound as in **day**.

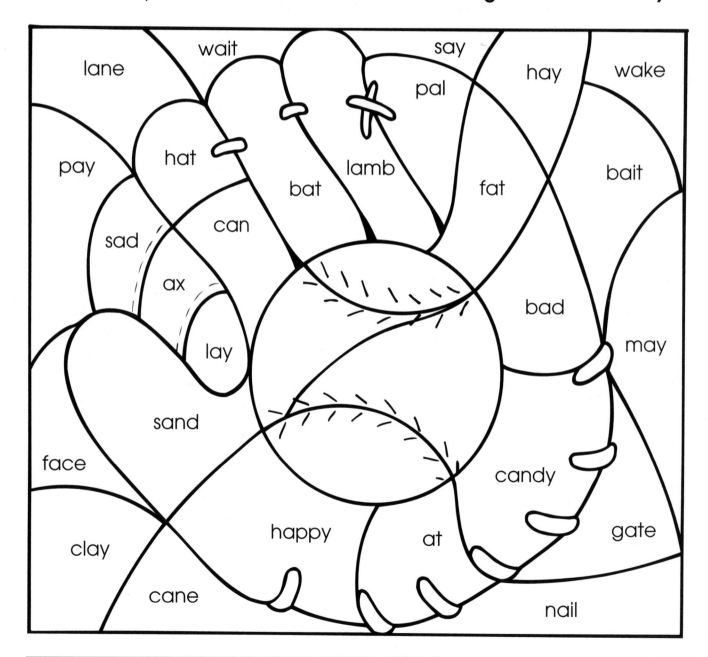

Show Me the Sign

Helen Keller was born on June 27. She had a serious illness when she was very young that left her blind and deaf. Through sign language and braille, she learned to communicate. Helen Keller went on to college and then spent her life helping others.

Sign language is a way to communicate using your hands. Use the code to find another name for sign language.

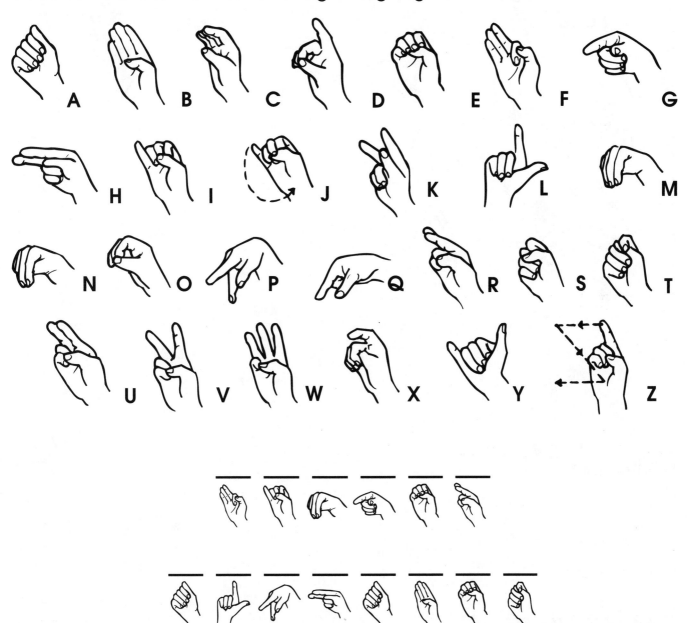

Name _____

Some Special Zoos

The Philadelphia Zoo in Pennsylvania was the first zoo in the United States. The Bronx Zoo in New York is the largest city zoo.

Connect the dots next to the animals in alphabetical order to find the largest land animal that lives in the zoo. Use the picture to solve the riddle below.

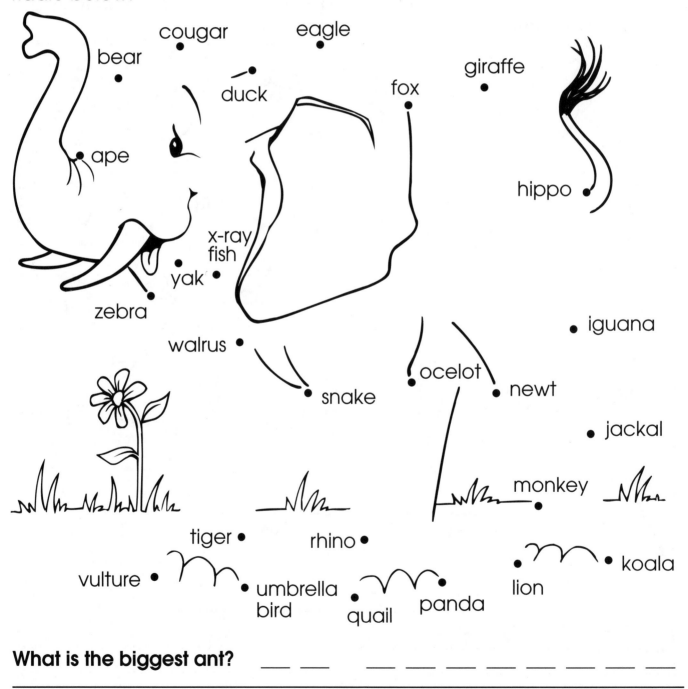

What is the biggest ant? __ __ __ __ __ __ __ __ __ __

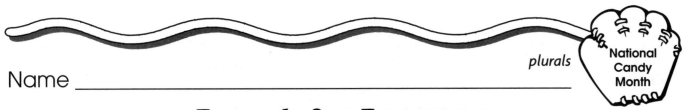

Name _____

Enough for Everyone

Candy is a special treat. To make sure there is enough for everyone, more than one piece of candy is needed. One way to make more candy is to change the **y** to **i** and add **es**.

Color each space red if you change the **y** to **i** and add **es** to make the word plural. Color each space blue if you add **es** to make the word plural. Color each space yellow if you add **s** to make the word plural.

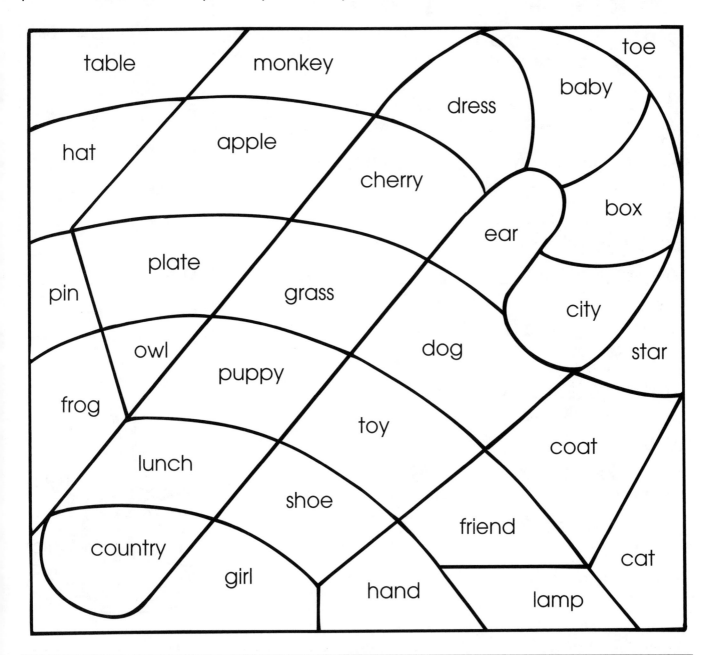

table   monkey   toe
dress   baby
hat   apple
cherry   box
ear
plate   city
pin   grass   star
owl   dog
puppy
frog   toy
coat
lunch
shoe   friend
country   cat
girl   hand   lamp

Name ____

One Nation

The Fourth of July is a celebration of our independence from England.

Use the code to fill in each missing letter. Then, to find out why it was said that George Washington had the largest family in America, write all the bold letters in order on the blanks below.

1. V ___ ___ ___ e y **F** ___ ___ ___ e
2. R ___ ___ ___ o **a** **t** s
3. P ___ ___ ___ a d ___ ___ ___ **h** i a
4. G **e** o **r** g e W ___ ___ ___ i n g t **o** n
5. **f** r ___ ___ ___ ___ m
6. R e v **o** l **u** ___ ___ ___ ___ a r y W a r
7. A ___ ___ **r** i **c** a
8. P a ___ ___ ___ **o** t s
9. **U** **n** ___ ___ ___ S ___ ___
10. P a **t** ___ ___ ___ k H ___ ___ **r** **y**

Code

a =	b =
c =	d =
e =	g =
h =	i =
l =	m =
n =	o =
p =	r =
s =	t =

He was the ___ ___ ___ ___ ___ ___ ___ ___

___ ___ ___ ___ ___ ___ ___ ___ ___ ___ ___!

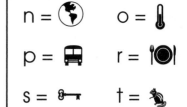

P.T. Barnum's Birthday

Name _____

The Greatest Show on Earth!

P.T. Barnum was born on July 5, 1810. He is known for starting the most famous circus in America.

Use the clues to complete each word family puzzle. Then, use the picture code to solve the riddle below.

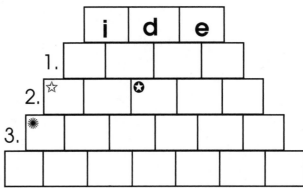

1. broad
2. a woman getting married
3. next to
4. opposite from inside

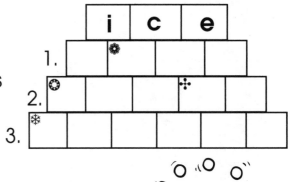

1. more than one mouse
2. another word for two times
3. a suggestion

1. ruler
2. something a bee does
3. after winter

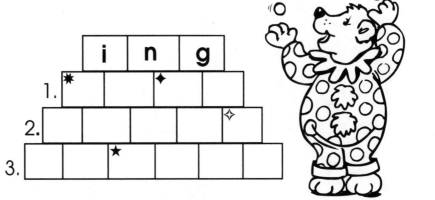

What happened to the kid who ran away with the circus? The police made him

☆ ★ ✿ ◆ ✧   ✪ ◎   ❋ ❄ ✛ ✴ !

Word Games: Grades 1–2

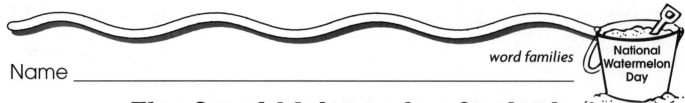

The Great Watermelon Contest

In August, during the annual Watermelon Fest in Hope, Arkansas, a seed-spitting contest is held. The person who spits a seed the farthest wins. Awards are also given to the highest, straightest, and funniest seed-spitters.

Color each flag if you can make a word by adding the beginning sound next to the word family on the watermelon. The contestant with the most flags colored is the winner.

-ap   c   cl   str   tr   br

-aw   j   fl   str   th   gr

-ate   l   pl   sk   st   gr

-ash   c   fl   tr   spl   sk

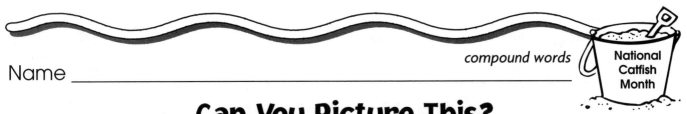

National Catfish Month

Name _____

Can You Picture This?

August is National Catfish Month. To celebrate, use the Word Bank to make compound words with **fish**. These are the names of real fish, but they do not really look like these pictures!

Word Bank				
sword	trumpet	trunk	cat	hog
clown	hatchet	lion	sun	star

___ ___ ___ ___ fish

___ ___ ___ fish

___ ___ ___ ___ fish

___ ___ ___ ___ ___ fish

___ ___ ___ fish

___ ___ ___ ___ fish

___ ___ ___ ___ ___ ___ fish

___ ___ ___ ___ fish

___ ___ ___ ___ ___ fish

___ ___ ___ fish

Back to School Month

Name _____

Back to School!

August is when most students return to school.

Read each clue. Use the Word Bank to fill in the blanks.

Word Bank					
balloon	moose	book	cooking	spoon	cool
wood	choose	football	pool	tooth	poor

1. rhymes with goose   __ __ __ __ __

2. neither warm nor cold   __ __ __ __

3. used for chewing   __ __ __ __ __

4. something you read   __ __ __ __

5. a sport   __ __ __ __ __ __ __ __

6. something filled with air   __ __ __ __ __ __ __

7. preparing food   __ __ __ __ __ __ __

8. used when eating   __ __ __ __ __

9. rhymes with lose   __ __ __ __ __ __

10. opposite of rich   __ __ __ __

11. rhymes with stood   __ __ __ __

12. a place to swim   __ __ __ __

To find out something about school, write the boxed letters in order on the blanks below.

__ __ __ __ __   __ __ __   __ __ __ __ __!

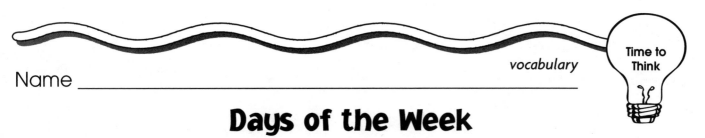

Name _____

Days of the Week

The days of the week come from Latin words.

Unscramble each day of the week using its abbreviation as a clue.

1. Fri.   Frdaiy   __ __ __ __ __ __

2. Tues.   daTueys   __ __ __ __ __ __ __

3. Sat.   atSruyda __ __ __ __ __ __ __ __

4. Thurs. yadTrhus __ __ __ __ __ __ __ __

5. Sun.   ndauSy   __ __ __ __ __ __

6. Mon.   danoMy   __ __ __ __ __ __

7. Wed.   ndesWeyda __ __ __ __ __ __ __ __ __

Write the days of the week in order.

_____   _____

_____   _____

_____

_____

Name _____

Months of the Year

Read each clue. Use the words from the Word Bank to fill in the blanks. Not all the words will be used.

Word Bank					
January	March	May	July	September	November
February	April	June	August	October	December

1. What month is before June but after April?

    — — —

2. What month is before August but after June?

    — — — —

3. What month is before May but after March?

    — — — — —

4. What month is before December but after October?

    — — — — — — — —

5. What month is before March but after January?

    — — — — — — — —

6. What month is before September but after July?

    — — — — — —

7. What month is before April but after February?

    — — — — —

8. What month is before July but after May?

    — — — —

9. What month is before October but after August?

    — — — — — — — — —

Name _____

A Jar of Many Colors

Jelly beans come in many colors, such as red, yellow, pink, orange, green, purple, and even black. Sometimes colors can have different names to describe them. For example, red is sometimes called cherry, yellow is called lemon, pink is called rose, and purple is called plum.

Color each jelly bean red if the word on it describes a color. Color all other jelly beans blue.

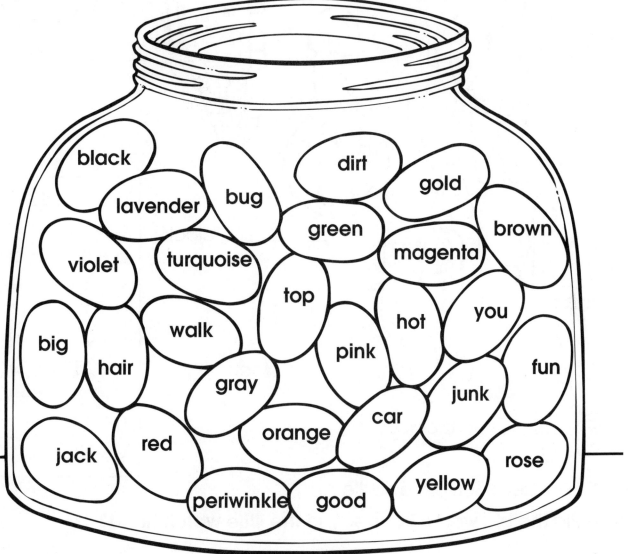

black, dirt, gold, lavender, bug, green, brown, violet, turquoise, magenta, top, you, walk, hot, big, pink, hair, gray, fun, junk, car, orange, jack, red, rose, periwinkle, good, yellow

To solve the riddle, unscramble the letters in the jelly bean. **What kind of bow cannot be tied?**

inowrba

a __ __ __ __ __ __

Which Watch?

Learning to tell time is important. One thing to remember is that the small hand tells the hour, and the large hand tells the minutes.

Write the time using number words.

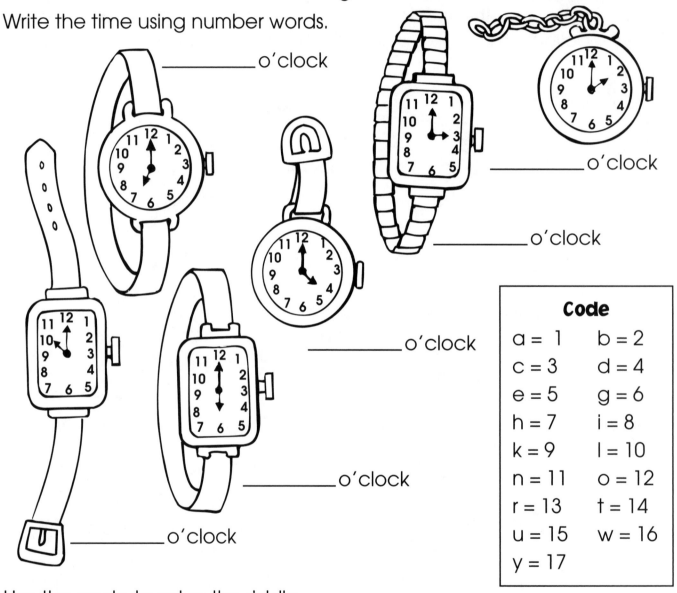

_____ o'clock

_____ o'clock

_____ o'clock

_____ o'clock

_____ o'clock

_____ o'clock

_____ o'clock

Code

a = 1	b = 2
c = 3	d = 4
e = 5	g = 6
h = 7	i = 8
k = 9	l = 10
n = 11	o = 12
r = 13	t = 14
u = 15	w = 16
y = 17	

Use the code to solve the riddle.

What did the big watch hand say to the little watch hand?

" __ __ __ __ , __ __ __ __ __ __ , __ __ __
  4 12 11 14   6 12   1 16 1 17   8 10 10

__ __ __ __ __ __ __ __ __ __ __ __ __ __ ."
2 5   2 1 3 9   8 11   1 11   7 12 15 13

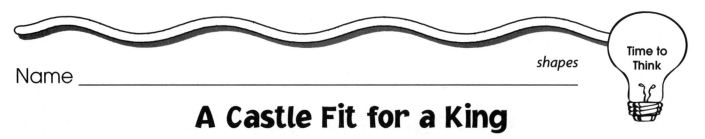

Name _____

A Castle Fit for a King

If you look carefully at buildings, you will notice many different shapes. Follow the directions to find all the shapes in the picture.

Color each rectangle red. Color each triangle green. Color each circle yellow. Color each square blue.

Name _____

Inching Along in Spring

Every spring you can see an inchworm crawling along. It crawls by pulling the back part of its body toward the front. An inchworm forms a loose cocoon and later appears as a moth.

Circle each word in the top row with the **short i** sound as in **twig**.

Circle each word in the bottom row with the **long i** sound as in **rice**.

1	2	3	4	5	6	7
big	rice	lie	list**e**n	**h**im	pine	line
tie	**c**hick	**d**ig	ice	tie	**in**ch	pin

8	9	10	11	12	13	14
mike	nine	wig	fin	**s**tripe	**w**hite	pig
fix	**n**apkin	**o**utside	**r**ice	pick	sick	right

Write each bold letter on the correct blank below to solve the tongue twister.

An ___ ___ ___ ___ ___ ___ ___ ___ ___ ___
    6 9 2 11 4 3 6 1 7 4

___ ___ ___ ___ ___ ___ ___ ___
6 9 2 5 13 10 11 8

___ ___ ___ ___ ___ ___ ___ ___ ___ ___ ___ ___ .
6 9 2 5 4 3   6 9 12 6 3 4

Time to Think

Name _____

Hopping Along

During the summer months, a pond is a hopping place.

Help the frog hop across the pond. Color each lily pad green if the word is in the **op** word family. Start with **hop**.

bit

chop

hop

chore

more

crop

score

fit

shore

snore

cot

flop

drop

stop

tot

knit

mop

not

chip

sit

pop

spot

hip

shop

lip

top

Time to Think

Name _____

Fall Colors

In the fall, the leaves of some trees turn bright colors before they die and fall to the ground.

Unscramble each word. Color each leaf red that has a word that begins with **t**. Color each leaf yellow that has a word that begins with **w**. Color each leaf orange that has a word that begins with **h**. Color each leaf green that has a word that begins with **f**.

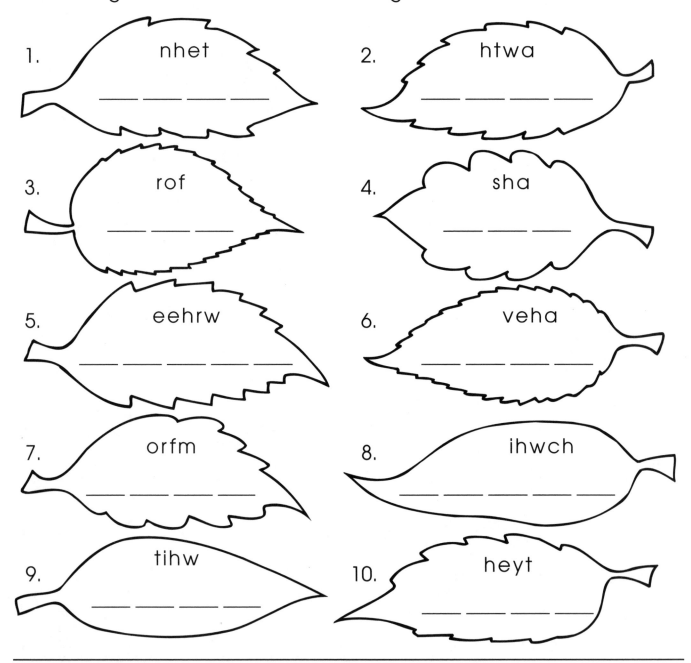

1. nhet
   ___ ___ ___ ___

2. htwa
   ___ ___ ___ ___

3. rof
   ___ ___ ___

4. sha
   ___ ___ ___

5. eehrw
   ___ ___ ___ ___ ___

6. veha
   ___ ___ ___ ___

7. orfm
   ___ ___ ___ ___

8. ihwch
   ___ ___ ___ ___ ___

9. tihw
   ___ ___ ___ ___

10. heyt
    ___ ___ ___ ___

Time to Think

Polar Bear

Polar bears live in the north along the frozen shores and icy waters of the Arctic Ocean. They have thick, white fur that blends in with the ice and snow.

Help Susie Bear slide down the snowy maze to find her cub, Sam. Follow the words that make new compound words with **snow**.

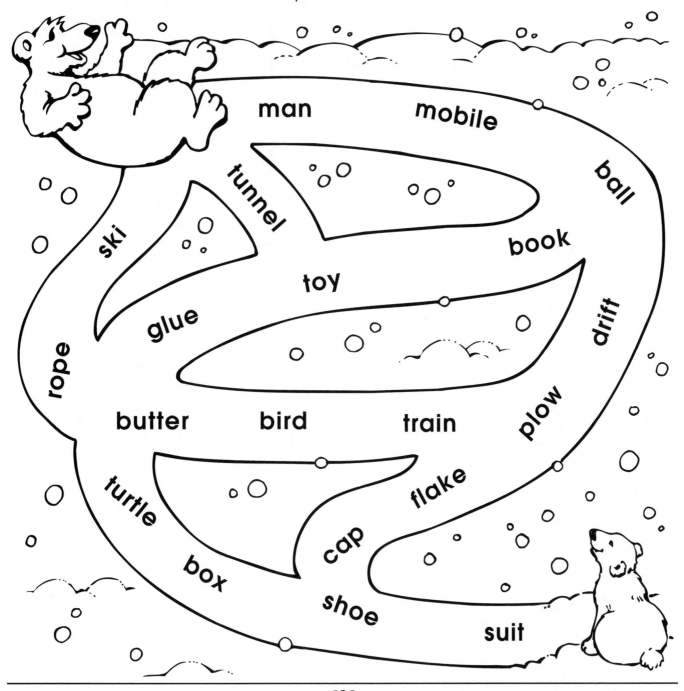

man   mobile   ball

tunnel   book

ski   toy

glue   drift

rope   book

butter   bird   train   plow

turtle   flake

cap

box   shoe

suit

Name _____

science vocabulary

How Many?

A body has many parts. There are two of some parts. Other parts have more than two. Write each word from the Word Bank in the correct space.

one

Word Bank

ears	tongue
ribs	eyebrows
teeth	toes
elbows	mouth
heart	nose
eyes	fingers

more than two

two

X and 0

To win tic-tac-toe, you want three in a row. Put an **X** on the words that go together in each game. Then, circle each tic-tac-toe.

Things That Go

bicycle	tax	dog
truck	house	car
train	hat	bud

Things to Wear

coat	jar	pants
socks	toe	dress
house	three	shoes

Things to Eat

car	book	yellow
cereal	pizza	cookie
potato	chest	egg

Sports

baseball	tennis	watch
home	football	land
turtle	soccer	wax

Weather

storm	night	rain
tornado	fog	snow
matter	vase	window

Animals

lion	snake	rock
sound	cow	build
zoo	further	tiger

Feelings

Follow the directions below.

1. Draw a square around the face that is the opposite of **sad**.

2. Circle the face that rhymes with brightened.

3. Draw two lines under the face that rhymes with **mad**.

4. Draw a triangle around the surprised face.

5. Draw an X through the face that rhymes with **sad**.

6. Draw a heart around the face that is doing something that rhymes with **dawn**.

Word Games: Grades 1–2

Name _____

Gum Balls

Fill in the blanks with a word that rhymes with the word on each gum ball.

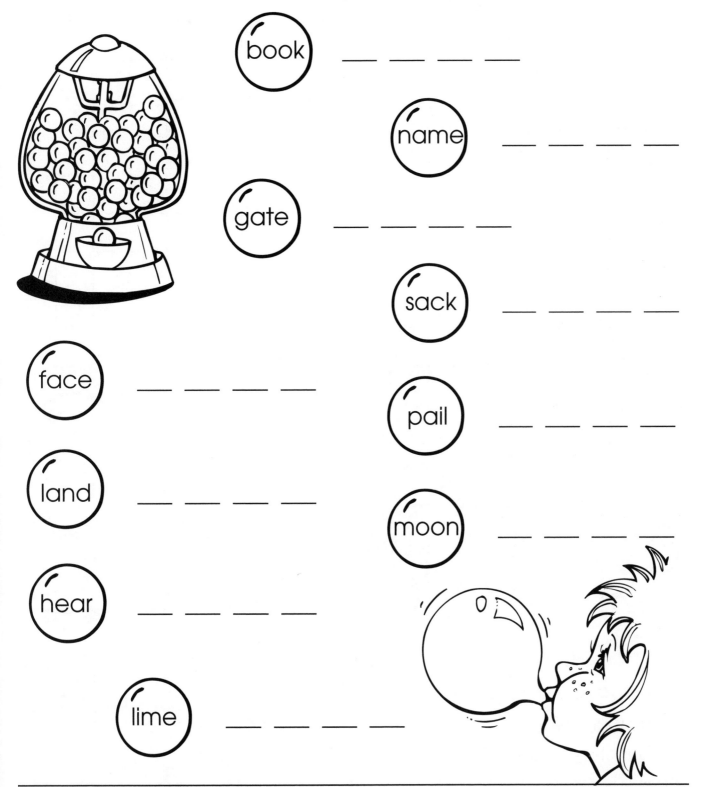

book ___ ___ ___ ___

name ___ ___ ___ ___

gate ___ ___ ___ ___

sack ___ ___ ___ ___

face ___ ___ ___ ___

pail ___ ___ ___ ___

land ___ ___ ___ ___

moon ___ ___ ___ ___

hear ___ ___ ___ ___

lime ___ ___ ___ ___

What Sport Is It?

Use each clue to complete the puzzle.

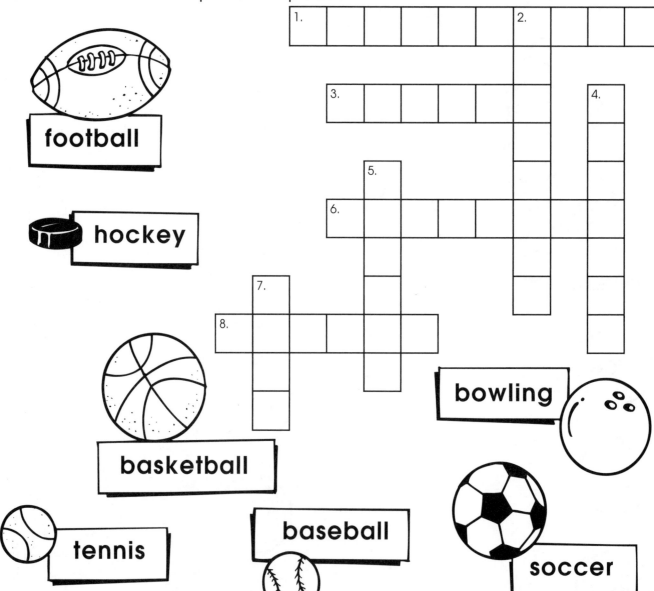

football

hockey

basketball

tennis

baseball

bowling

soccer

golf

Across

1. Make a basket!
3. Good serve!
6. Touchdown!
8. Shoot the puck!

Down

2. Hit a home run!
4. Spare!
5. Kick a goal!
7. Hole in one!

Word Games: Grades 1–2

Name _____

Holiday Fun

Read each clue. Use the words from the Word Bank to fill in the blanks.

Word Bank
Halloween   Thanksgiving   Valentine's Day
Independence Day   Presidents' Day

1. a day we celebrate the birthdays of Lincoln and Washington

2. a day when children in costumes go trick-or-treating

3. a day for giving hearts to people we care about

4. a holiday also called the Fourth of July

5. a day of feasting and giving thanks

1. __ __ __ __ __ __ __ __ __ __ __ , __ __ __ __

2. __ __ __ __ __

3. __ __ __ __ __ __ __ __ , __ __ __

4. __ __ __ __ __ __ __

5. __ __ __ __ __ __

Write the circled letters in order to solve the riddle. **What fruit has been known since man invented the calendar?** __ __ __ __ __

First-Grade Reading Vocabulary

These words have been carefully selected as the high-frequency words usually used in first-grade reading materials.

after	buy	drink	goes	jump	move	rain	still	us
again	by	drop	going	just	much	ran	stop	use
all	call	during	good	keep	must	read	street	walk
along	came	easy	got	kept	my	ready	such	want
am	can	eat	grab	kick	myself	red	sun	was
an	cannot	eight	gray	kid	name	ride	take	way
and	can't	end	green	land	near	road	tell	we
ant	car	fall	had	last	need	round	ten	week
are	child	far	has	laugh	net	run	than	well
as	clap	fast	have	lay	next	said	thank	went
at	class	fat	he	leave	nine	same	that	were
back	clear	father	head	left	no	sang	the	wet
bad	clock	fed	hello	leg	not	sat	their	what
bag	cold	feel	help	less	now	saw	them	when
bake	color	feet	her	let	odd	say	then	where
ball	come	first	here	lie	of	says	there	which
band	cot	fish	hill	like	off	see	they	while
bat	could	fit	him	lip	often	seen	they're	white
bath	cut	five	his	long	oh	set	thing	who
be	dad	fix	hit	look	old	seven	think	why
because	dark	flag	hold	lost	on	shall	this	will
bed	day	flat	hole	low	once	she	three	win
been	dead	food	home	lunch	one	should	thumb	wind
before	dear	foot	hop	mad	only	show	time	wish
best	desk	for	hot	made	or	sick	to	with
big	did	four	house	make	orange	side	today	won't
bike	didn't	fox	how	man	other	sister	together	would
bit	dig	friend	I	may	our	sit	told	wrong
black	dime	from	if	me	out	six	tomorrow	year
blue	dish	fun	in	meet	pet	sixteen	too	yellow
both	do	game	inch	men	pick	sixth	took	yes
bottom	does	gave	into	milk	pink	sleep	top	yet
box	doesn't	get	is	mix	play	slow	toy	you
boy	dog	girl	isn't	mom	plus	small	tree	your
bread	done	give	it	moon	pull	so	try	
brown	don't	given	it's	more	push	some	turn	
bus	down	giving	job	most	put	soon	two	
but	drank	go	joy	mother	quick	soy	up	

Second-Grade Reading Vocabulary

These words have been carefully selected as the high-frequency words usually used in second-grade reading materials.

able	ask	blanket	busy	chose	cream	dropped	feed
about	asleep	blew	butter	chosen	creek	drug	fell
above	ate	block	button	church	creep	drum	fellow
absent	awake	blow	buzz	circle	cried	drunk	felt
across	away	boat	cage	circus	cross	dry	fence
act	awhile	body	camp	city	crow	dust	fever
action	baby	boil	candle	claim	crowd	each	few
add	bait	bone	candy	clay	crush	ear	fifth
address	balloon	book	capital	clear	crust	early	fifty
adventure	bank	boot	card	climb	cry	earn	fight
afraid	bark	born	care	close	curl	earth	fill
after	barn	bother	careful	closet	curtain	east	finally
afternoon	barrel	bottle	carry	clothes	dance	egg	find
again	base	bought	case	cloud	danger	eight	fine
against	basket	bow	cash	clown	dangerous	eighth	finger
age	bathe	brain	catch	coat	date	eighty	first
agree	bean	brake	caught	coil	deep	either	flew
ahead	bear	bread	cent	collar	desert	eleven	flight
air	beautiful	break	center	collect	dessert	else	float
alike	beauty	breakfast	certain	common	different	empty	floor
almost	been	breath	chain	continue	dinner	enjoy	flour
alone	began	breathe	chair	control	direction	enter	flower
already	begin	brick	chance	cook	dirt	evening	fly
always	begun	bridge	change	cool	discover	ever	fold
among	behind	bright	chapter	cord	distance	every	follow
amount	believe	bring	charm	corn	doll	example	fool
angry	bell	broken	chase	corner	dollar	excited	football
animal	below	brook	chasing	correct	door	exercise	forget
another	bend	broom	cheap	count	double	expect	forgot
answer	beneath	brother	cheat	country	drag	explain	fork
any	bent	brought	check	county	draw	eye	forty
apart	better	build	cheek	couple	dream	face	fought
arm	bicycle	built	cherry	cow	dress	fair	found
army	bill	bump	chest	cracks	drew	family	fourteen
around	birthday	bunch	children	crawl	drive	farmer	fourth
arrow	bite	burn	chin	crayon	driver	farther	free
art	blame	bury	choose	crazy	driving	fear	fresh

Second-Grade Reading Vocabulary (continued)

frighten	head	interest	light	monkey	over	please	right
front	health	interesting	line	month	owl	plenty	ring
fry	heard	jelly	listen	more	own	point	river
full	heart	join	little	morning	owner	poison	rode
funny	heaven	jungle	live	motor	pack	poor	roll
furniture	heavy	king	load	mountain	paid	post	room
further	heel	kiss	locate	mouse	pair	potato	root
gas	held	kite	lock	muddy	pants	pound	rope
gate	helpful	kitten	loose	nail	paper	pour	row
geography	hen	knee	lose	nap	parents	power	rule
giant	hid	knew	loud	nature	park	practice	rush
gift	hide	knight	louder	necessary	part	pray	sack
giving	high	knock	love	needle	party	pretty	sad
glad	hip	know	luck	neighbor	pass	price	safe
glass	holiday	known	lying	neither	passed	print	safety
goose	hollow	ladder	maid	new	past	probably	sail
grade	honest	lady	mail	nice	patch	problem	sale
grass	hood	lake	manner	nickel	path	proud	salt
great	hook	lamb	many	night	pay	pull	sand
grew	hopeful	lamp	matter	ninety	peace	puppy	sandwich
grip	hopped	large	maybe	noise	pear	purple	saucer
ground	horn	late	meal	noisy	pen	quart	save
grow	horse	lately	mean	none	pencil	question	school
grown	hose	later	measure	noon	penny	quiet	science
guess	hour	laundry	meat	north	people	quit	score
hair	hug	law	merry	northern	perfect	quite	scratch
half	hundred	lawn	message	nose	perhaps	race	scream
hall	hung	lead	mice	note	period	rack	season
hammer	hungry	leader	middle	nothing	person	rainy	seat
hand	hunt	leaf	mild	number	phone	raise	second
handle	hurry	lean	mile	ocean	pie	rake	seed
hang	hurt	leave	million	o'clock	piece	rang	seen
happen	husband	lend	mind	office	pile	reader	self
happy	ice	length	mine	oil	pill	ready	sell
hard	idea	letter	minute	once	pillow	receive	send
hardly	ill	library	mirror	only	place	remember	sent
hat	important	lick	miss	open	plain	rest	sentence
have	include	life	mistake	ourselves	plane	return	separate
hay	inside	lift	moment	outside	plant	rice	seventh

Second-Grade Reading Vocabulary (continued)

seventy	small	stole	thirsty	understand	woman
several	smart	stone	thirteen	until	women
shade	smile	stool	those	used	won
shake	smooth	store	thought	useful	wonderful
shall	snow	storm	thousand	using	wood
shape	soak	story	threw	vacation	wooden
share	socks	street	throat	very	wool
sharp	soft	string	through	visit	word
shed	soil	strong	throw	visitor	wore
shelf	son	stuck	thrown	voice	work
shell	song	study	thumb	wagon	world
shine	sore	sudden	tie	wait	worn
ship	sorry	sugar	tied	wake	worry
shirt	sound	sum	tight	wall	worse
shoe	sour	summer	tiny	wash	worst
shoot	space	sunny	title	water	wrap
shop	special	super	toad	wave	wrist
shore	spell	supper	toe	weak	writer
short	spend	suppose	ton	weigh	written
shout	spent	sure	tonight	west	wrong
shower	spill	sweet	tool	wheel	wrote
sight	spin	swim	tooth	wherever	yard
sign	spoke	table	toward	whether	yesterday
silence	spoon	tail	town	which	you
silent	sport	taken	train	whip	young
silly	spot	taste	treat	whole	
silver	spring	taught	trick	whom	
simple	square	teach	trouble	whose	
since	stairs	teacher	truck	wide	
sing	stamp	team	true	wife	
single	start	teeth	truly	wild	
sir	state	tenth	truth	window	
sixty	stay	terrible	twelve	windy	
size	steal	thankful	twenty	wing	
skin	steam	these	twice	winter	
skirt	step	thick	ugly	wire	
sky	stick	thin	unable	wise	
slap	sting	thing	uncle	without	
slide	stir	third	under	woke	

Flash Card Activities

Flash cards are a great way for students to learn and memorize new vocabulary words. Make copies of the flash card pattern below.

Word Family Flash Cards

Write a word on the front of the flash card. Cut out or draw a picture of that word to put on the back of the card. Students can practice the words independently using the pictures to check their answers.

Silly Sentences

Make flash cards of nouns, verbs, and adjectives. Mix them up and have students choose several cards to write silly sentences.

Concentration Game

Choose words from the reading vocabulary lists. Make two sets of the same words on the flash cards. Ask students to shuffle the flash cards and lay them face down on the table in rows. Have students take turns turning over two cards at a time, looking for two cards that match. When a student finds a match, another turn can be taken. Continue play until every flash card has been matched. The student with the most matches wins.

Read and Spell

Choose words from the reading vocabulary lists and write them on the cards. Place a flash card on a table. Ask a student to identify the word. Turn over the flash card and ask the student to spell the word or write it on another sheet of paper. For evaluation purposes, write an **R** for **Reading** and an **S** for **Spelling** in the corner of each card. When that skill has been mastered, circle the letter.

Flash Card Pattern

Vocabulary Activities

Vocabulary development is an important skill for students of all ages. The following activities are designed to strengthen students' vocabularies.

Vocabulary Notebooks

Feature a new word each day. Have the students use notebooks to write the word featured in a sentence and illustrate it. Encourage the students to use word three times during the day—either orally, in writing, or by finding it in a book. Keeping notebooks is a great way to keep track of new words learned and to use for review.

Mini-Books

Have students make mini-books using word families. Encourage them to illustrate and to share their stories. This will build fluency and increase their confidence in themselves as readers.

Vocabulary Bingo

Use the flash card pattern on page 114 to make clue cards for bingo. Write the vocabulary words from the flash cards on the generic bingo card. During play have the students the flash cards and search for the matching vocabulary words on their bingo cards. Buttons, beans, or bingo chips may be used as game pieces.

Word Searches

Word searches help build fluency by enabling students to isolate words within the text. Use the generic puzzle on page 116 to make your own classroom puzzles. Use words from different subject areas such a spelling, social studies, and science for the puzzle. Remind students that words may appear across, up, down, and diagonally in the puzzle.

Vocabulary Words
Bingo Card #____

Free Space

Word Search

Word Bank

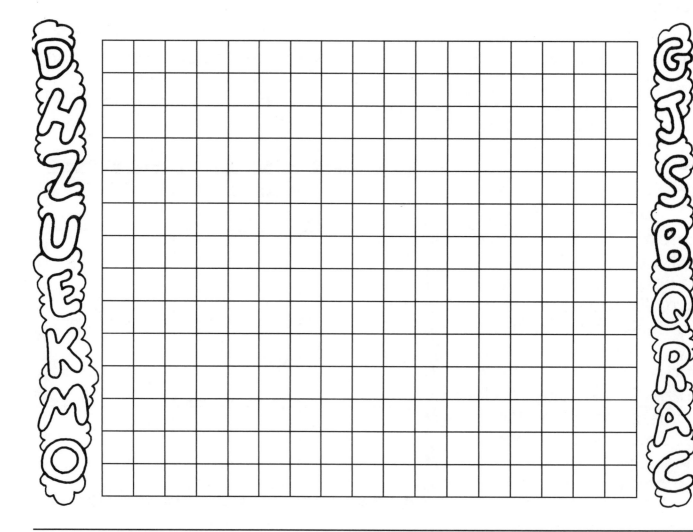

Page 4
Tools of the Trade
Labor Day is celebrated the first Monday of September. It is a day to honor working Americans.
Write the correct letter in each space using the code below.

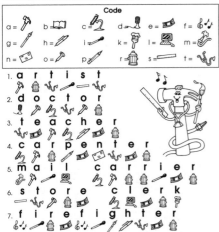

Code

a =	b =	c =	d =	e =	f =
g =	h =	i =	k =	l =	m =
n =	o =	p =	r =	s =	t =

1. a r t i s t
2. d o c t o r
3. t e a c h e r
4. c a r p e n t e r
5. m a i l   c a r r i e r
6. s t o r e   c l e r k
7. f i r e f i g h t e r

Page 5
Family Tree
The first Sunday after Labor Day is Grandparent's Day. This is the day we celebrate our grandparents by sending a card or giving a hug to show them how much they mean to us.

Use the Word Bank to help find the words in the family tree. The words go across and down.

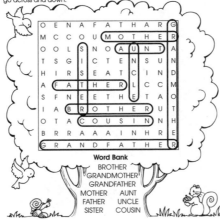

Word Bank
BROTHER
GRANDMOTHER
GRANDFATHER
MOTHER   AUNT
FATHER   UNCLE
SISTER   COUSIN

Page 6
The Great Bathtub Race
Every September in Nome, Alaska, contestants race down the street in bathtubs filled with sudsy water for the Great Bathtub Race.

Color each square that contains letters that make a word when added to the word family in the bathtub. The bathtub with all the squares colored wins!

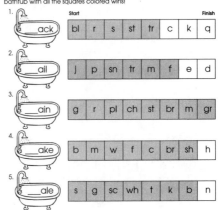

1. ack — Start: bl r s st tr c k q Finish
2. ail — j p sn tr m f e d
3. ain — g r pl ch st br m gr
4. ake — b m w f c br sh h
5. ale — s g sc wh t k b n

Page 7
Baby Farm Animals
Some farm animals have special names for their young. Unscramble the letters to find out the names of the baby animals.

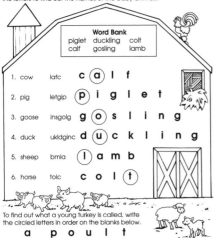

Word Bank
piglet   duckling   colt
calf   gosling   lamb

1. cow   lafc   c a l f
2. pig   letgip   p i g l e t
3. goose   insgolg   g o s l i n g
4. duck   ukldginc   d u c k l i n g
5. sheep   bmla   l a m b
6. horse   tolc   c o l t

To find out what a young turkey is called, write the circled letters in order on the blanks below.
a   p o u l t

Page 8
Celebrate Native Americans
The fourth Friday in September is American Indian Day. Follow the directions below to discover where some tribes used to live.

Color each space brown if the word makes the **long e** sound as in **see**. Color each space blue if the word makes the **short e** sound as in **west**.

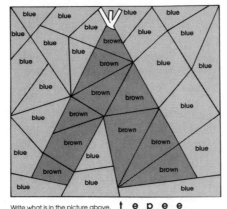

Write what is in the picture above.   t e p e e

Page 9
Doggy Days
National Dog Week is in September. Dogs are one of the most popular pets in the United States.

Use the picture clues to write the short vowel words.

1. p w i g
2. d l o g
3. j b e d t
4. d f i s h   s h
5. l s o c k   c k
6. l s t a m p   m p

Write each shaded letter on the matching numbered blank below to solve the riddle.

What do you step in when it rains cats and dogs?
p o o d l e s
1 2 2 4 6 3 5

Page 10
Let's Hit a Home Run!
Baseball is America's favorite pastime.

Step up to the plate and hit a home run by using the clues to complete the puzzle.

Word Bank
notebook   raindrop   firewood   outdoors
headache   homesick   railroad   football
footstep

1. opposite of indoors — o u t d o o r s
2. a sore head — h e a d a c h e
3. a place to write a note — n o t e b o o k
4. where a train travels — r a i l r o a d
5. a sport — f o o t b a l l
6. missing home — h o m e s i c k
7. footprint — f o o t s t e p
   f i r e w o o d
   r a i n d r o p

To solve the riddle, write the letters in the shaded boxes in order on the blanks below.
Why does it take longer to run from second base to third base than from first base to second base?

When you run from second to third base there is a
s h o r t s t o p in the middle.

Page 11
You Are Playing My Song!
September is National Piano Month. Did you know that there are 88 keys on the piano? The white keys number 52, and the black keys number 36.

Use the code to find the **ay** words, like in **play**.

1. d a y
2. a w a y
3. m a y b e
4. c l a y
5. c r a y on
6. to d a y
7. y e s t e r d a y
8. g r a y
9. f r e e w a y

Page 12
Keys to Good Manners
Are you respectful? Do you treat others the way you want to be treated? Are you polite and courteous? These are all keys to good manners.

Help Andrew find the key to the treasure of the city of Good Manners. Circle the words that people use to show good manners.

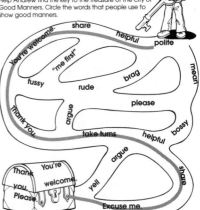

share   helpful   polite
You're welcome.   "me first"   brag   mean
fussy   rude
Thank you.   please
argue   take turns   helpful   bossy
argue
Thank you.   You're welcome.   yell   share
Please.   Excuse me.

Page 13

Alphabet Soup

Everyone should eat healthy every day. Healthy eating makes our bodies grow big and strong. Some of the healthiest foods are vegetables.

Make some alphabet soup by unscrambling the vegetable words below and circling them in the pot of soup. The words go across and down.

1. rractor **c a r r o t**
2. abnse **b e a n s**
3. isonon **o n i o n s**
4. tatopo **p o t a t o**
5. orcn **c o r n**
6. koar **o k r a**
7. eleryc **c e l e r y**
8. spae **p e a s**

Page 14

Space Age

On October 4, 1957, the Space Age began with the launch of *Sputnik*, the first man-made satellite.

Unscramble the words in each rocket. Write each circled letter on the blank above the correct number to solve the riddle.

Word Bank
star
comet
planet
space
moons
orbit

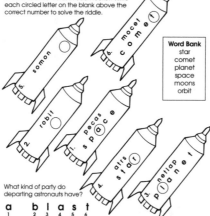

somon, mocel comet, robit, pecas space, alrs star, netilap planet

What kind of party do departing astronauts have?

a b l a s t
1 2 3 4 5 6

Page 15

Up the Ladder

The second week of October is Fire Prevention Week. Help Firefighter Fred put out the fire by solving the puzzle.

Start with the word at the bottom of each ladder. Change only one letter to make a new word. You must end up with the word at the top of the ladder.

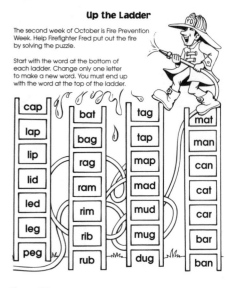

cap	bat	tag	mat
lap	bag	tap	man
lip	rag	map	can
lid	ram	mad	cat
led	rim	mud	car
leg	rib	mug	bar
peg	rub	dug	ban

Page 16

Yum! Yum!

National Dessert Day is in October. Celebrate this day by eating your favorite dessert!

Homophones are words that sound alike but have different spellings and different meanings. Choose the correct homophone in each sentence. Use the homophones you chose to complete the puzzle.

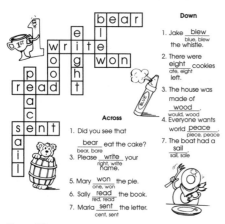

Crossword answers: bear, write, won, read, sent, sail, peace

Down
1. Jake __blew__ the whistle.
   blue, blew
2. There were __eight__ cookies left.
   ate, eight
3. The house was made of __wood__.
   would, wood
4. Everyone wants world __peace__.
   piece, peace
7. The boat had a __sail__.
   sail, sale

Across
1. Did you see that __bear__ eat the cake?
   bear, bare
3. Please __write__ your name.
   right, write
5. Mary __won__ the pie.
   one, won
6. Sally __read__ the book.
   red, read
7. Maria __sent__ the letter.
   cent, sent

Page 17

Flip-Flop, Hippity-Hop

Celebrate National Poetry Day by solving the puzzle. Some poems use words like "Humpty-Dumpty" or "Itsy-Bitsy Spider."

Use the Word Bank to fill in the blanks to make a new word. Find the word that you wrote and circle it in the word search. The words go across and down.

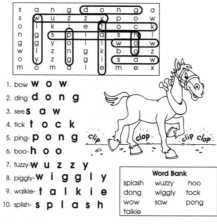

1. bow **w o w**
2. ding **d o n g**
3. see **s a w**
4. tick **t o c k**
5. ping- **p o n g**
6. boo- **h o o**
7. fuzzy- **w u z z y**
8. piggly- **w i g g l y**
9. walkie- **t a l k i e**
10. splish- **s p l a s h**

Word Bank
splash, wuzzy, hoo
dong, wiggly, tock
wow, saw, pong
talkie

Page 18

Turn It On!

October 21 is Edison Lamp Day. Thomas Edison did not actually invent the light bulb, but in 1879 he perfected one in 1879.

Light up each light bulb by circling the word that has an **opposite** meaning from the underlined word.

1. more / many / **less**
2. out / outside / **in**
3. stop / **go** / end
4. low / bottom / **high**
5. fat / heavy / **thin**
6. good / great / **bad**
7. down / under / **up**
8. quiet / silent / **loud**
9. little / small / **big**

To solve the riddle, write the **bolded** letters in order on the lines below.
What kind of bulb does not need water?

l i g h t b u l b

Page 19

United Together

The United Nations is a group of countries that work together for world peace and a better way of life for all people. October 24 is United Nations Day.

Make new words by using the letters in **United Nations**. Use the Word Bank to help you fill in the blanks.

tent, oats, dent
satin, ten
so, tune
son, inn
edit, nut
untie
unit e, ant, end

Word Bank
tent, dent, so, inn, ten
untie, tune, ant, end, nut
satin, son, edit, oats, unite

Page 20

Candy Treats

Fill your bag with candy by solving the puzzle below.

Use the clues to find the words that go together like "trick or treat."

Word Bank
found, tell, shine, never, forth
write, clear, sound, go, seek

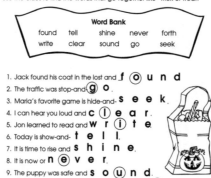

1. Jack found his coat in the lost and **f o u n d**
2. The traffic was stop-and **g o**
3. Maria's favorite game is hide-and- **s e e k**
4. I can hear you loud and **c l e a r**
5. Jon learned to read and **w r i t e**
6. Today is show-and- **t e l l**
7. It is time to rise and **s h i n e**
8. It is now or **n e v e r**
9. The puppy was safe and **s o u n d**
10. The ball bounced back and **f o r t h**

To solve the riddle, write each circled letter in blank above the correct number.

What position does a monster play on a soccer team?
g h o u l i e
2 10 1 9 4 5 8

Page 21

Corn Popping Treats

Corn is one of the most important crops grown in the United States. When you heat a kernel of corn, it will pop. Then you have popcorn! October is National Popcorn Poppin' Month.

Use the letters in the pieces of popcorn to make words on each **word family** bag.

-eat: **m e a t**, **w h e a t**, **c h e a t**

-ell: **c e l l**, **s p e l l**, **s h e l l**

-est: **v e s t**, **r e s t**, **c r e s t**

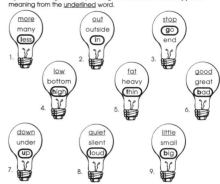

Page 22

"Dino" Might

Dinosaurs are giant reptiles that lived millions of years ago.

Unscramble each word in the dinosaur eggs by writing the **syllables** in the correct order on the blanks in the puzzle.

1. tile rep
2. od pe ri
3. ant gi
4. est larg
5. sil fos
6. lions mil
7. ri ter ble
8. ry his to
9. ture crea
10. cov dis ery

1. r e p t i l e
2. p e r i o d
3. g i a n t
4. l a r g e s t
5. f o s s i l
6. m i l l i o n s
7. t e r r i b l e
8. h i s t o r y
9. c r e a t u r e
10. d i s c o v e r y

What would you get if you crossed a pigeon, a frog, and a prehistoric monster? Hint: The answer is in the puzzle above.

a p i g e o n - t o e d dinosaur

Page 23

Counting Votes

Election Day is the first Tuesday after the first Monday in November. This is when we vote for people to run our government.

Read the clues given by each student to see who has the most votes for class president. Below each student, write the number that tells how many votes that student received.

I have six less votes than Tara.

The number of votes I received is an even number between six and ten.

I have three less votes than Amy.

I have two more votes than Amy.

I have five more votes than Sam.

f o u r — Sam

e i g h t — Amy

f i v e — Josh

t e n — Tara

n i n e — Ty

Circle the student with the most votes.

Page 24

May I Have a Sandwich, Please?

Sandwich Day is observed in November. To celebrate, let's make some super sub sandwiches.

Make each sandwich by starting with the word at the bottom. Remove the letter that is on each slice of bread. Use the remaining letters to make a new word.

a	t
at	e
eat	h
heat	c
teach	

an	t
ant	s
ants	p
pants	l
plants	

I	t
it	s
sit	e
ties	d
tides	

I	h
hi	s
his	t
hits	n
hints	

Page 25

Where Would You Go?

The United States is made up of 50 states.

Use the Word Bank to solve the riddles.

Pennsylvania | Oregon
Washington | Montana
Tennessee | New Hampshire

1. What state would you go to if you had a huge pile of dirty clothes? W a s h i n g t o n
2. What state would you go to if you needed a dime? T e n n e s s e e
3. What state would you go to if you wanted to lie out in the sun? M o n t a n a
4. What state would you go to if you wanted to write a letter? P e n n s y l v a n i a
5. What state would you go to if you were a miner? O r e g o n
6. What state would you go to if you wanted a sandwich? N e w H a m p s h i r e

Page 26

Hello!

November 21 is World Hello Day! Saying hello is a nice way to be friendly to others.

Use the Word Bank to fill in the blanks with **vowels** to learn how to say hello in eight different languages. Then circle the words in the puzzle. they go across and down.

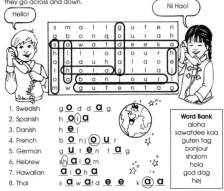

1. Swedish   g o d d a g
2. Spanish   h o l a
3. Danish   h e j
4. French   b o n j o u r
5. German   g u t e n t a g
6. Hebrew   s h a l o m
7. Hawaiian   a l o h a
8. Thai   s a w a t d e e k a a

Word Bank
aloha
sawatdee kaa
guten tag
bonjour
shalom
hola
god dag
hej

To find out how to say good-bye in Hawaiian, write the circled letters in order on the blanks. a l o h a
5 2 3 6 1

Page 27

Are You Puzzled?

Everyone loves the challenge of a word box puzzle. In celebration of National Game and Puzzle Week, see if you can solve these puzzles. The word box puzzle reads the same across as it does down.

Use the clues to complete the puzzles.

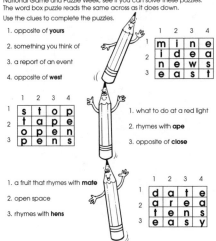

1. opposite of **yours**
2. something you think of
3. a report of an event
4. opposite of **west**

	1	2	3	4
1	m	i	n	e
2	i	d	e	a
3	n	e	w	s
4	e	a	s	t

	1	2	3	4
1	s	t	o	p
2	t	a	p	e
3	o	p	e	n
	p	e	n	s

1. what to do at a red light
2. rhymes with **ape**
3. opposite of **close**

1. a fruit that rhymes with **mate**
2. open space
3. rhymes with **hens**

	1	2	3	4
1	d	a	t	e
2	a	r	e	a
3	t	e	n	s
	e	a	s	y

Page 28

A Lion's Roar

A lion was first exhibited in America in Boston in 1716.

Unscramble each names of a zoo animal and write it in the puzzle. Use the Word Bank to help. Then write each shaded letter in order to solve the riddle below.

Word Bank
penguin | panda | turtle
snake | toucan | goat
platypus | giraffe | bear

1. earb
2. danpa
3. ucanto
4. ffeagir
5. atypsupl
6. pgennui
7. ttlure
8. kaesn
9. tago

1. b e a r
2. p a n d a
3. t o u c a n
4. g i r a f f e
5. p l a t y p u s
6. p e n g u i n
7. t u r t l e
8. s n a k e
9. g o a t

August was the name of a monkey who was always picking on larger animals. One day he got into an argument with a lion. The next day was the first of September. Why?

because it was the e n d o f A u g u s t

Page 29

Strutting Turkey

Thanksgiving is celebrated in the U.S. on the fourth Thursday in November. It is a time to share and give thanks for the things one has.

Color each feather red if the word makes the **short a** sound as in **thank**.
Color each feather yellow if the word makes the **long a** sound as in **ate**.
Color each feather purple if the word makes the **short u** sound as in **cut**.
Color each feather orange if the word makes the **long u** sound as in **huge**.

5. face yellow
6. orange orange
4. cube orange
7. hand red
3. drum purple
8. hay yellow
2. plate yellow
9. cut purple
1. snack red
10. blue orange

Write the underlined letters above the correct numbers below to solve the riddle.

What kind of key will not open a door? a t u r k e y
9 10 3 1 6 8

Page 30

Nature's Aviators

November is Aviation History Month. It celebrates the building and flying of aircraft.

Find the words in the dot-to-dot to complete each sentence below. Write them on the lines. Then connect the dots in the order of your answers to make a picture of nature's best aviators.

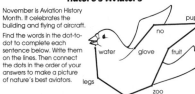

1. Fly is to air as swim is to w a t e r.
2. Bird is to wings as dog is to l e g s.
3. Up is to down as top is to b o t t o m.
4. Cow is to farm as lion is to z o o.
5. Carrot is to vegetables as apple is to f r u i t.
6. Cat is to kitten as dog is to p u p p y.
7. Hot is to cold as yes is to n o.
8. Foot is to sock as hand is to g l o v e.

Write the circled letters above that match the correct numbers to solve the riddle. Who invented the first airplane that did not fly?

the w r o n g Brothers
1 5 3 7 8

119 Word Games: Grades 1-2

Page 31

Brightest Star

On December 3, 1621, Galileo refined the telescope. A telescope magnifies distant objects. It is used to study planets and stars. Sirius is the brightest star.

Color each star yellow if it contains a word with the same vowel sound as "star."

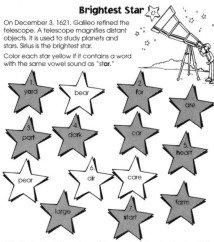

1. yard
bear
2. far
are
3. part
4. dark
car
5. heart
pear
air
care
large
6. start
farm

Write the bolded letters above the correct numbers to solve the riddle.

a s t a r f i s h
1 1 7 3 1 2 6 7 5

Page 32

Wonderful World of Disney

Walt Disney was born December 5, 1901. He was one of the most famous motion picture producers in history.

Read the clues to find out some of Walt Disney's favorite characters. Circle them in the word search.

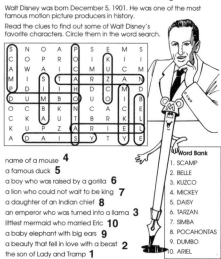

name of a mouse **4**
a famous duck **5**
a boy who was raised by a gorilla **6**
a lion who could not wait to be king **7**
a daughter of an Indian chief **8**
an emperor who was turned into a llama **3**
littlest mermaid who married Eric **10**
a baby elephant with big ears **9**
a beauty that fell in love with a beast **2**
the son of Lady and Tramp **1**

Word Bank
1. SCAMP
2. BELLE
3. KUZCO
4. MICKEY
5. DAISY
6. TARZAN
7. SIMBA
8. POCAHONTAS
9. DUMBO
10. ARIEL

Page 33

Walks with a Waddle

When the South Pole was discovered on December 14, 1911, penguins were found. Penguins cannot fly, but they are great swimmers. Penguins have very short legs and walk with a waddle.

Use the clues to write the words that end with **ie** as in **waddle**, in the puzzle. Then write the letters in each shaded box in oder to finish the sentence below.

Word Bank		
needle	bottle	people
turtle	kettle	single
rattle	simple	double

1. baby's toy
2. something a baby drinks from
3. two of the same
4. something you boil water in
5. a group of men and women
6. a reptile with a shell
7. one
8. something you sew with
9. easy

r a t t l e
b o t t l e
d o u b l e
k e t t l e
p e o p l e
t u r t l e
s i n g l e
n e e d l e
s i m p l e

Penguins build their nests and raise their young in huge colonies called
r o o k e r i e s.

Page 34

Tea Party

The Boston Tea Party was a raid by American colonists who dressed up like Indians and threw 342 chests of tea into the Boston Harbor to avoid being taxed.

Color the chest brown if you add **s** to make the word plural.
Color the chest yellow if you add **es** to make the word plural.
Color the chest green if you have to change the last letter to **i** and add **es** to make the word plural.

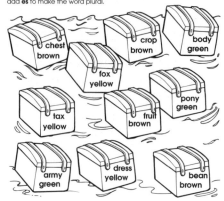

chest brown
crop brown
body green
fox yellow
tax yellow
pony green
fruit brown
army green
dress yellow
bean brown

Page 35

Short Stack

Potato latkes are a traditional Hanukkah food. These pancakes are fried in oil. The oil is a reminder of Hanukkah miracle.

Write the word from the Word Bank that is the last part of one compound word and the first part of a different compound word.

Word Bank
ball book fly fish bee man light yard down

butter **fly** paper
sta(r) **fish** tail
su(n) **light** house
honey **bee** hive
post **man** hole
ba(c)k **yard** stick
sun **down** town
b(a)se **ball** room
coo(k) **book** cas(e)

To solve the riddle, write the circled letters in order on the blanks.
What kind of cake do you eat for breakfast? **p a n c a k e**

Page 36

Get a Clue

The first crossword puzzle appeared in the *New York World* newspaper on December 21, 1913.

Match the shape of the state to find its name in the puzzle.

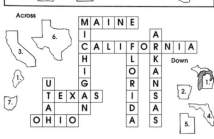

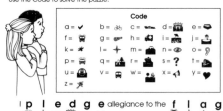

Across

M A I N E
C A L I F O R N I A
U T E X A S
O H I O

Down

Page 37

Hung with Care

Some people hang stockings on their fireplaces in hopes that Saint Nicholas will come and fill them with toys.

Answers will vary.

1. Draw a bright colored beach ball on the first, fourth, sixth, and ninth stockings.
2. Draw a candy cane on the second, fifth, and tenth stockings.
3. Draw a star on the third, seventh, and eighth stockings.
4. Write girls' names and draw red stripes on the stockings that follow the first, third, sixth, and eighth stockings.
5. Write boys' names and draw green stripes on the first, third, sixth, eighth, and tenth stockings.
6. What stocking does not have a name on it? **fifth** Write your name on that stocking.

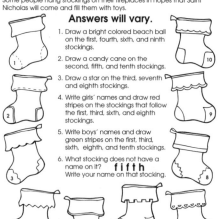

Page 38

Let's Make a Mkeka!

Kwanzaa is an African-American holiday that celebrates the African festival of the harvest of the first crop. Kwanzaa means "first fruits" in Swahili. Mkeka means "placemat."

Color the space red if the word is a fruit.
Color the space green if the word is a vegetable.
Color the space black if the word is neither.

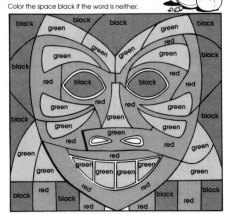

Page 39

One Nation

The Pledge of Allegiance was recognized on December 28, 1945. It was recommended that all schoolchildren should recite it every day before starting school.

Use the Code to solve the puzzle.

Code				
a =	b =	c =	d =	e =
f =	g =	h =	i =	j =
k =	l =	m =	n =	o =
p =	q =	r =	s =	t =
u =	v =	w =	x =	y =
z =				

I p l e d g e allegiance to the f l a g
of the U n i t e d States of America and to
the r e p u b l i c for which it stands,
one n a t i o n under God, indivisible, with
l i b e r t y and
j u s t i c e for all.

Word Games: Grades 1–2

Page 40

Happy New Year!

January 1st is the beginning of a new year. It is called New Year's Day.

Write the correct number words in the blanks. Then use the letters on the calendar to solve the riddle.

January

Sun.	Mon.	Tues.	Wed.	Thurs.	Fri.	Sat.
			a one	b two	c **three**	d four
e **five**	f six	g seven	h **eight**	i nine	j **ten**	k eleven
l twelve	m **thirteen**	n fourteen	o **fifteen**	p **sixteen**	q seventeen	r **eighteen**
s nineteen	t **twenty**	u twenty-one	v **twenty two**	w twenty-three	x **twenty four**	y **twenty five**
z twenty-six	**twenty seven**	**twenty eight**	twenty-nine	thirty	**thirty one**	

What does a caterpillar do on New Year's Day?

t u r n s o v e r a
20 21 14 19 15 22 5 18 1

n e w l e a f !
14 5 23 12 5 1 6

Page 41

Clean That Messy Desk!

Everyone likes to get organized to start the year off right. The second Monday in January is National Clean Off Your Desk Day.

Unscramble the letters to find the names of things you might have on your desk. Write the words in the correct boxes below.

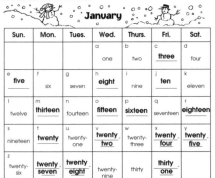

1. epn
2. kobo
3. reapp
4. racony
5. srreesa
6. cenipl
7. arths
8. doof
9. abg

1. p e n
2. b o o k
3. p a p e r
4. c r a y o n
5. e r a s e r s
6. p e n c i l
7. t r a s h
8. f o o d
9. b a g

Page 42

A Hug a Day

January 21 is National Hug Day. The best way to celebrate this day is to hug your mom and dad or someone special to you.

Mom and Dad are palindromes. They are words spelled exactly the same, forward and backward. Circle the palindromes in the sentences.

1. (Sis) loves hugs, too.
2. Give a hug to the baby (pup).
3. Give three people a hug at (noon).
4. (Lil) had a bear hug on her (bib).
5. Sam hugged the puppy named (Otto).
6. (Bob) (did) a good (deed) and got a hug.
7. (Dad) hugged the (kayak) so he would not fall off.

Circle the phrases that are palindromes.
1. Jessica's hug earned the (top spot).
2. The (race car) named Bear-Hug won.

Can you figure out the palindrome phrase?
no l e m o n , no melon

Page 43

Are You Sick?

National School Nurse Day is a time when we should appreciate our nurses at school. They take care of us when we feel sick.

Color the tongue depressor red if it makes a word when you add **ick**.

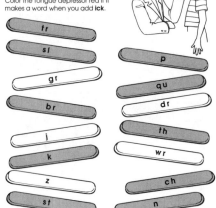

tr
sl
gr
br
j
k
z
st

p
qu
dr
th
wr
ch
n

Page 44

Gold Rush

Throughout history people have wanted to strike it rich. On January 24, 1848, gold was discovered in California.

Discover more about money by using the Word Bank to complete the puzzle.

Word Bank

ten	cent	nickel	dollar
quarter	one	five	penny
dime	coins	twenty	

Down
1. 8 quarters and 3 dollar bills are equal to one _____ -dollar bill.
2. Paper money is called _____ bills.
3. 1¢
5. ¢
7. Dimes, nickels, pennies, and quarters are called _____.
9. Two five-dollar bills are equal to one _____-dollar bill.

Across
2. 10¢
4. 25¢
6. 5¢
8. Two ten-dollar bills
10. Four quarters equal ___ dollar

f i v e
d i m e
d o l l a r
p e n
q u a r t e r
n n y
n i c k e l
c e n t
o t w e n t y
i e
n o n e
s

Page 45

Let's Make Music!

Mozart week is the last week in January. Mozart was one of the greatest and most creative musical composers in history. Mozart was composing music at the age of five!

Color each space yellow if the word names a musical instrument. Color all the other spaces blue.

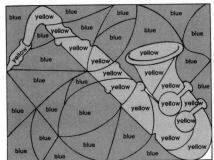

Use the code to solve the riddle.
What kind of phone makes music?
a s a x o p h o n e

Code

a e h n o p s x

Page 46

Stick to It!

On January 31, 1928, cellophane tape was invented. This great invention has made our lives easier, as it can hold many things together. How else could you wrap a present?

Solve the rebus puzzle with words with the same long **a** sound as **tape**. Stick to it!

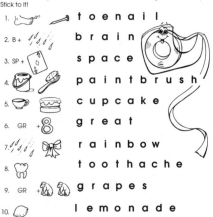

1. t o e n a i l
2. B + b r a i n
3. SP + s p a c e
4. p a i n t b r u s h
5. c u p c a k e
6. GR + g r e a t
7. r a i n b o w
8. t o o t h a c h e
9. GR + g r a p e s
10. l e m o n a d e

Page 47

Um, Good!

When it is cold outside, it feels good to eat something hot to keep warm inside. January is National Soup Month.

Use the clues to write words the letter sounds make. Use the Word Bank if you need help.

Word Bank

tepee	peel	bee
empty	pea	easy
seal	buy	see
while	you	deal

Read the words in the box to solve the riddle.
1. not hard — EZ
2. water animal — CL
3. banana's skin — PL
4. period of time — YL
5. vegetable — P
6. kind of insect — B
7. pass out cards — DL
8. kind of tent — TP
9. to look — C
10. pronoun — U
11. to purchase — BY
12. not full — MT

e a s y
s e a l
p e e l
w h i l e
p e a
b e e
d e a l
t e p e e
s e e
y o u
b u y
e m p t y

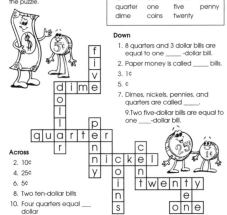

When do you swallow your words?
When you eat a l p h a b e t s o u p !

Page 48

Curl Up with a Good Book

January is National Book Month. It is a time for everyone to find a good book and curl up in a comfy spot and read.

Circle the word in each worm section that rhymes with the top word. Then solve the riddle by writing the circled letters in order on the blanks.

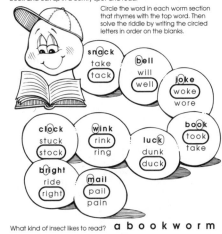

sn(a)ck — take / (tack)
(b)ell — will / (well)
j(o)ke — (woke) / wore
cl(o)ck — stuck / (stock)
(w)ink — (rink) / ring
b(o)ok — (took) / take
(b)right — ride / (right)
(m)ail — (pail) / pain
l(u)ck — dunk / (duck)

What kind of insect likes to read? a b o o k w o r m

Page 49

Chinese New Year

China's biggest celebration is Chinese New Year. It falls between January 21 and February 19. This holiday is celebrated with parades, fireworks, and traditional family meals. Each new year has an animal that represents that year.

Circle the word that has the same vowel sound as each animal in the Chinese zodiac.

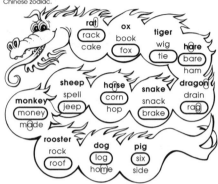

To find out the name of an old Chinese puzzle, write the circled letters in order.

t a n g r a m

Page 50

Groundhog Day

According to tradition, a groundhog is awakened from its winter sleep on February 2nd. If it sees its shadow and goes back into its den, there will be six more weeks of winter.

Use the clues to find the names of other animals that sleep in the winter.

1. It begins like 🏀 and rhymes with 🍐
   b e a r

2. It begins like 🐌 and rhymes with 🍰
   s n a k e

3. It begins like ✏️ and rhymes with ⚙️
   f r o g

4. It begins like 🚲 and rhymes with 🐱
   b a t

5. It begins like 🔝 and rhymes with 🛣️
   t o a d

6. It begins like 🪑 and rhymes with ⛷️
   t u r t l e

7. It begins like 🎣 and rhymes with 🥧
   f l y

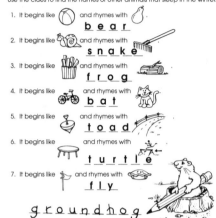

g r o u n d h o g

Page 51

Be A Weather Whiz

February 5 is Weatherman's Day. Another name for weatherman is meteorologist, a person who forecasts and reports the weather.

Be weather-wise and use each clue to solve the puzzle.

Word Bank
wind tornado snow clouds
rain lightning hail rainbow

Across
3. a bow of colors in the sky
4. looks like marbles made of ice
6. small, white crystals
8. drops of water falling from the sky

Down
1. sometimes called a twister
2. tiny drops of water and specks of dust in the sky
5. electric spark during a storm
7. moving of air

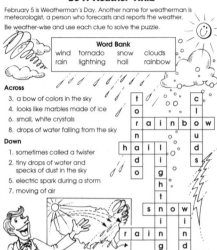

Page 52

Candy Hearts

February 14 is Valentine's Day. It is celebrated by giving cards, and candy to someone special.

Color the hearts with words with the **hard c** sound, like **candy**, red.
Color the hearts with words with the **soft c** sound, like **special**, pink.

Write the circled letters on the hearts in order to solve the riddle.
What did the postage stamp say to the envelope on Valentine's Day?

I AM STUCK ON YOU!

Page 53

Amazing Astronaut

In 1962, John Glenn orbited Earth three times in a space capsule. When the automatic controls failed, John Glenn had to take control of the capsule.

Connect the dots in ABC order.

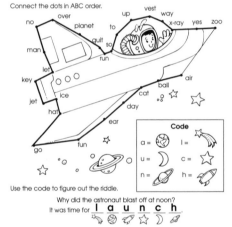

Code
a = 🌍   l = ☄️
u = 🌙   c = ⭐
n = 🪐   h = 🚀

Use the code to figure out the riddle.

Why did the astronaut blast off at noon?
It was time for **l a u n c h**

Page 54

Presidents' Day

Presidents' Day is the third Monday in February. This day is set aside to observe the birthdays of Abraham Lincoln (February 12) and George Washington (February 22).

Use the clues to find which president's portrait is on each bill.

Code
a = 🦅   c = 🌍   d = 🎱   e = ⚖️   f = 🐛   g = 🏹   h = 🔦
i = 🐟   j = 🔨   k = 🔑   l = ✈️   m = 🐴   n = 🐱   o = 🌙
r = 🚢   s = 🔔   t = 👁️   v = 🐦   w = ✂️   y = ♥️

1. $2
2. $50
3. $20
4. $5
5. $500
6. $1,000
7. $5,000
8. $1

JEFFERSON
GRANT
JACKSON
LINCOLN
McKINLEY
CLEVELAND
MADISON
WASHINGTON

Read down the circled letters to find out who is on the ten dollar bill.

Page 55

Famous African-Americans

In the month of February, famous African- Americans are celebrated. These people have contributed to America and have made this nation a better place.

Circle the last name of each political leader, athlete, and entertainer.

Circle the first name or initials of each writer, educator, scholar, and civil rights leader. Then find each circled name or initials in the puzzle. They go across and down.

Athletes	Entertainers	Writers, Educators, and Scholars
Magic Johnson	Oprah Winfrey	Booker T. Washington
Jackie Robinson	Miles Davis	Mary McLeod Bethune
Jackie Joyner-Kersee	Denzel Washington	Gwendolyn Brooks
		Maya Angelou

Civil Rights Leaders
Martin Luther King
Rosa Lee Parks
W.E.B. DuBois

Political Leaders
Colin Powell
L. Douglas Wilder
Condoleezza Rice

(word search puzzle grid)

Page 56

The Heart of the Matter

February is American Heart Month. Eating right and exercising are good for your heart.

Color the spaces red that name things that make your heart beat faster. Color the spaces blue that name things that make your heart beat slower.

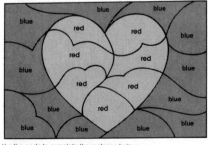

Use the code to complete the sentence below.

Code
c = ✏️   e = 🐟   h = 🎱   i = 🐚   m = 🐴   n = 🦅   t = 👁️   u = 🌙

The heart pumps the entire body's blood supply through the body every **m i n u t e**.

Page 57

Brush Your Teeth

You need your teeth to break up and chew food. Brushing your teeth and gums after meals and before bed helps keep them strong and healthy.

A number of 6-letter words contain double letters in the middle. Use the clues to help you complete the words.

1. hare
   r a bb i t
2. something you hit a nail with
   h a mm e r
3. laugh
   g i gg l e
4. nighttime meal
   d i nn e r
5. something you look into
   m i rr o r
6. something a dog wears
   c o ll a r
7. a baby cat
   k i tt e n
8. opposite of **winter**
   su mm e r
9. a color
   ye ll o w
10. opposite of **rough**
    s m oo t h

Write the circled letters in order.
George Washington wore a set of false teeth made partly of
r h i n o c e r o s ivory.

Page 58

Oink! Oink!

On March 1, pigs are squealing all over the country. It is National Pig Day. Let's give all the pigs three big oinks. Oink! Oink! Oink!

Use the clues to solve the puzzle. All the words have **ink** somewhere in them.

Word Bank

sink	blink	stinks
twinkle	sprinkle	wrinkle
drink	pink	shrink

1. opposite of float
2. to close and open your eyes
3. smells badly
4. something a star does
5. light rain
6. crease in the skin
7. to make smaller
8. to take a sip of
9. a color

1. s i n k
2. b l i n k
3. s t i n k s
4. t w i n k l e
5. s p r i n k l e
6. w r i n k l e
7. s h r i n k
8. d r i n k
9. p i n k

Write the letters in the shaded boxes on the correct blanks to solve the riddle.

What telephone number does a pig call instead of nine-one-one when it gets into trouble ?

s w i n e -one-one
3 4 5 6 6

Page 59

Tip Your Hat to the Cat!

Dr. Seuss was born March 2, 1904. He was a famous author of nearly 50 children's books, including *Hop on Pop* and *The Cat in the Hat*.

Circle the words that rhyme with the first word. Then write a new word on the space that also rhymes with the first word.

Answers will vary.

wrong — right, along
quick — quiet, pick
three — there, knee

song — read, road, lead
lick — bring, broke, king
tree — lawn, paw, yawn

feed — dress, pass, mess
sing — those, hose, these
mass — (those, hose, these)
fawn — mail, mall, snail

less
rose
tail

To find out what book Dr. Seuss wrote using fewer than fifty words, write the bolded letters in order on the blanks below.

G r e e n   E g g s   a n d   H a m

Page 60

Hello, Who Is This?

Alexander Graham Bell was born March 3, 1847. He invented the telephone. On March 10, 1876, the first words were heard over a telephone.

To find out what Bell said to his assistant, Thomas Watson, solve the puzzle using the telephone. Remember, for each number you have a choice of three letters.

C O M E   H E R E,
3 6 6 3   4 3 7 3

W A T S O N .   I
2 8 7 7 6 6   4

N E E D   Y O U !"
6 3 3 3   9 6 8

Page 61

Size It Up!

We use weights and measures all the time to describe the amounts or sizes of things. Some of the first measurements were based on the human body. One foot originally was the length of a person's foot. Now it is 12 inches. One yard was the distance from the nose to the fingertip. Now it is three feet, or 36 inches.

Find the words on the measuring tools in the puzzle and circle them.

inch	foot	yard

meter	centimeter

gram, kilogram
ounce, pound, ton
cup, pint, quart, gallon, liter

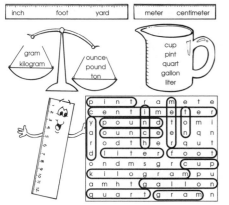

```
p i n t r a m e t e
c e n t i m e t e r
y p o u n d t o m i
a o u n c e n q n
r o d t h e r q u t
d l i t e r f o o t
o n d m s g r c u p
k i l o g r a m p u
a m h t g a l l o n
q u a r t g r a m
```

Page 62

Pot of Gold Coins

Legend has it that at the end of the rainbow, there is a pot of gold.

Help the leprechaun find his pot of gold by coloring the coins yellow if the word makes the **oi** sound as in **coin**.

join, gold, lion
soil, hour, worst
storm, choice, above
boil, worn
noise, loud, wait
raise
void, poison, point

Page 63

Seal Appeal

March 18 is the International Day of the Seal. Everyone should enjoy seals that day and learn more about them. Seals are very smart animals—smart enough to learn to balance a ball on their nose.

Write the missing letters by using the vowels, **a, e, i, o,** and **u** to make words.

Answers will vary.

f i sh
j a b
n e w
b o w
a ct
enj o y
dr o p
dr u m
sw i m
l u ck
b e nt

Make a list of five other words you could have made by using a different vowel.

Page 64

Family Fun

National Family Day is a day when we should take time to do something fun as a family.

To find a fun family activity, follow the directions.

Color clothing words yellow.   Color food words blue.
Color toy words black.   Color furniture words red.

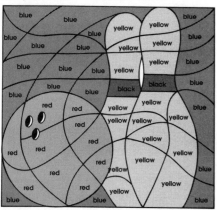

Page 65

We Are What We Eat!

Eating the right foods is important. To help people choose the right foods, the U.S. government developed a food pyramid.

Write each word from the Word Bank by the correct space in the food pyramid.

Word Bank					
vegetables	fats	fruits	breads	dairy	meats

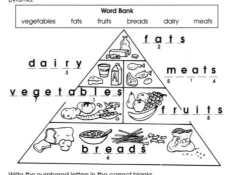

f a t s
2

d a i r y
3

m e a t s
5   1   4

v e g e t a b l e s
7

f r u i t s
8

b r e a d s
6

Write the numbered letters in the correct blanks.

The foods at the bottom of the pyramid are the ones you should eat in

the l a r g e s t amounts. At the top are the foods
7 5 1 2 3 1 6
you should eat in the s m a l l e s t amounts.
4 5 2 1 1 6 4 8

Page 66

Easter

On Easter, many children like to go on Easter egg hunts.

Write each word from the Word Bank next to the correct clue. Then to answer the riddle below, write the circled letters in order on the blanks.

1. goes well with peanut butter
2. what chicks hatch from
3. a candy flavor
4. white puffy treat
5. rhymes with sandy
6. young rabbit
7. something to hold things in
8. green and grows in the ground
9. a kind of hat
10. baby chickens

1. j e l l y
2. e g g s
3. c h o c o l a t e
4. m a r s h m a l l o w
5. c a n d y
6. b u n n y
7. b a s k e t
8. g r a s s
9. b o n n e t
10. c h i c k s

Word Bank
chocolate
marshmallow
jelly
candy
chicks
grass
bonnet
eggs
basket
bunny

What does the Easter bunny plant in his garden?

j e l l y   b e a n s

Page 67

Peter's Prank

It is April Fools' Day, and Peter celebrated by playing a prank on Mrs. Frank's class. Peter took all the fish out of two fish tanks.

Help Peter put the fish back in the right tanks. Use the blends to make new words. If the fish makes a word by adding **ank**, color the fish green, and write the words in the **ank** bowl. If the fish makes a word by adding **ake** color the fish blue and write the word in the **ake** bowl.

ank

ake

blank	brake
clank	flake
plank	drake
spank	snake
prank	stake

Page 68

Plant a Tree

Arbor Day is celebrated in the spring. Often it is observed by planting a tree. A tree is home to many animals.

The letters on some of the acorns can make new words by adding **unk**. See how many words you can make.

tr unk

Answers will vary.

bunk
chunk
dunk
junk

plunk
shrunk
skunk
stunk

Page 69

Ocean Animals

The National Week of the Ocean is in April. The blue whale is the largest animal in the ocean. In fact, it is the largest animal in the world.

Use the Word Bank to find the names of other ocean animals. Circle them in the puzzle. To solve the riddle look for a word going down in the puzzle.

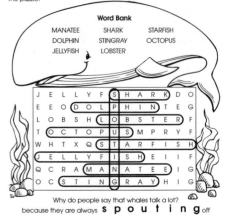

Word Bank

MANATEE	SHARK	STARFISH
DOLPHIN	STINGRAY	OCTOPUS
JELLYFISH	LOBSTER	

Why do people say that whales talk a lot?

because they are always **s p o u t i n g** off

Page 70

Reduce, Reuse, and Recycle

Celebrate Earth Day by recycling.

Write the things in the puzzle made with recycled materials.

Recycled paper
newspaper
cereal boxes
wrapping paper
cardboard

Recycled metal
cars
cans
nails
bicycles

Recycled plastic
soda bottles
cameras
benches
shoes
carpeting

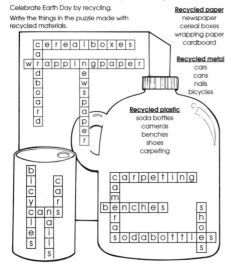

Page 71

Don't "Fowl" Up!

James Audubon spent his life studying and painting birds.

Some birds' names have smaller words in them. For example, the word **crow** has **row** in it. Use the Word Bank to answer the questions.

Word Bank

bluejay	goldfinch	pelican	robin	turkey
cardinal	jackdaw	pheasant	sandpiper	

1. What bird has stealing in its name? **r o b i n**
2. What bird has a boy's name in its name?
   j a c k d a w
3. What bird has a metal container in its name?
   p e l i c a n
4. What bird has a musician in its name?
   s a n d p i p e r
5. What bird can get into locked places? **t u r k e y**
6. What bird has an automobile in its name?
   c a r d i n a l
7. What bird is worth a lot? **g o l d f i n c h**
8. What bird has a color in its name? **b l u e j a y**
9. What bird has a tiny insect in its name?
   p h e a s a n t

Our national bird is the **b a l d   e a g l e**.

Page 72

Be Honest

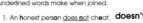

Honesty means to tell the truth. An honest person is also sincere and keeps promises. An honest person does not steal, cheat, or behave in a tricky manner.

Write the contraction that each pair of underlined words make when joined.

1. An honest person <u>does not</u> cheat. **doesn't**
2. <u>It is</u> important to keep your promises. **It's**
3. <u>She is</u> truthful. **She's**
4. <u>We are</u> doing our best to be loyal. **We're**
5. <u>I will</u> always tell the truth. **I'll**
6. <u>We will</u> promise to be honest. **We'll**
7. <u>You are</u> to always do the right thing. **You're**
8. Cathy <u>does not</u> steal. **doesn't**

To find out a famous saying, write the bolded letters in order on the blanks below.

H o n e s t y   i s   t h e
b e s t   p o l i c y !

Page 73

It All Adds Up!

Math plays an important part in everyone's life. We use some kind of math skill every day. We use math to tell time and to buying things at the grocery store.

Use the clues to solve the crossword puzzle.

Across

1. eleven, thirteen, _____, seventeen
6. Twenty minus seven equals _____.
7. Two plus one equals _____.
8. Fifteen minus eight equals _____.

Down

1. Twelve plus two equals _____.
2. two, four, six, _____, ten
3. Three plus seven equals _____.
4. Six plus two plus four equals _____.
5. Ten minus three minus one equals _____.
6. five, ten, fifteen, _____, twenty-five

Page 74

Better Be Safe

March is National Youth Sports Safety Month. It is always important to follow the rules and be careful when playing sports or playing on a playground.

To find out one piece of sports equipment you should always wear when roller blading, riding your bike, or hitting a baseball, follow the directions.

Color each word red that has another word hidden in it. The words **I** and **a** do not count. Color all other words blue.

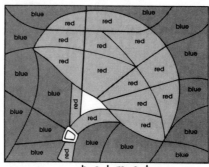

You should always wear a **h e l m e t**.

What word is hidden in it? **m e t** (Answers will vary.)

Page 75

Get Set, Go!

Every few seconds, a brand new car comes out of a car factory somewhere in the world.

To see what car comes off the assembly line first, color each block that makes a word when the blend in the box is put before the word family on the car. The car that makes the most words is the winner!

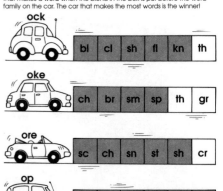

ock

| bl | cl | sh | fl | kn | th |

oke

| ch | br | sm | sp | th | gr |

ore

| sc | ch | sn | st | sh | cr |

op

| ch | cr | dr | sh | st | fl |

Page 76

Grin and Giggle

Grab your funny bone because the month of March is National Humor Month.

Answer the questions to solve the riddle.

1. the letter before b **a**
2. the letter after k **l**
3. the letter between o and q **p**
4. the letter after g **h**
5. the letter before b **a**
6. the letter before c **b**
7. the letter between d and f **e**
8. the letter before u **t**
9. the letter before t **s**
10. the letter after n **o**
11. the letter between t and v **u**
12. the letter after o **p**

What is abcdefghijklmnopqrstuvxyz, slurp? Someone eating

a l p h a b e t   s o u p

Use the code to solve the sentence that contains all 26 letters of the alphabet.

The five wild boxing zebras jump quickly

Code		
a = ✦	b = 🚲	c = ⚑
d = ⛵	e = 🏆	f = 🚗
g = ☂	h = 🐛	i = 🎄
j = ✈	k = 🐾	l = 🐿
m = 🎧	n = ◆	o = ▢
p = 🎈	q = 🐸	r = 🐞
s = 🐟	t = 🦋	u = 🐱
v = 🚙	w = 🐠	x = 🐈
y = 📟	z = 🌍	

Page 77

May Flowers

April showers bring May flowers. Celebrate May Day by planting beautiful flowers.

Write as many compound words as you can by using the words on the petals of both flowers.

Answers will vary.

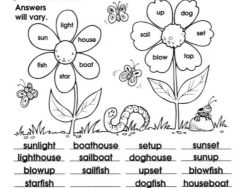

sunlight	boathouse	setup	sunset
lighthouse	sailboat	doghouse	sunup
blowup	sailfish	upset	blowfish
starfish		dogfish	houseboat

How do you rate?

| 14 or more | excellent | 8 to 13 | good |
| 4 to 7 | fair | 1 to 3 | Try again! |

Page 78

It's a Celebration!

Cinco de Mayo is a Mexican holiday. It is the celebration of the victory of the Mexican Army over the French in the Battle of Puebla on May 5, 1862.

Circle the English words in the puzzle from the Word Bank that come from the Spanish language. The words will go across and down.

Word Bank	
BANANA	MUSTANG
BRONCO	COYOTE
CANYON	CORRAL
TOMATO	COWBOY
RODEO	COCOA
PATIO	CHILI

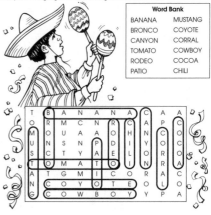

Page 79

Most Unusual Pets

Unusual pets are becoming more popular.

To find some of the most popular unusual pets, write the beginning letter of each picture word in the blanks.

1. **g e r b i l**
2. **s n a k e**
3. **p o t b e l l y** pig
4. **p a r r o t**
5. **i g u a n a**
6. **s p i d e r**
7. **g e c k o**
8. **r a b b i t**

The most popular dog breed registered by the American Kennel Club in 2000 was the **l a b r a d o r** retriever.

Page 80

Teacher's Gift

On Teachers' Day, Mrs. Lee's class decided to bring her gifts to show how much she is appreciated but they forgot to label them.

Each gift rhymes with the name of the student who brought it. Use the Word Bank to write the correct names on the tags.

Word Bank			
Jess	Ray	Matt	Kelly
Scott	Jake	Randall	Heather
Noelle	Ben	Blair	Dan

Scott, Noelle, Jess, Dan, Randall, Ray, Ben, Jake, Kelly, Heather, Blair, Matt

Page 81

Happy Mother's Day

Our mothers are very special to us. We honor them on the second Sunday in May.

Use the Word Bank to solve the following analogies.

Word Bank					
children	eight	lost	mice	near	red
soft	south	teeth	two	won	

1. Goose is to geese as mouse is to **mice**
2. Sail is to sale as too is to **two**
3. Dark is to light as found is to **lost**
4. Man is to men as child is to **children**
5. Wood is to would as read is to **red**
6. Fast is to slow as far is to **near**
7. Blew is to blue as ate is to **eight**
8. East is to west as north is to **south**
9. Pare is to pear as one is to **won**
10. Happy is to sad as hard is to **soft**
11. Foot is to feet as tooth is to **teeth**

To find the name of one of the most famous mothers in literature, write the circled letters in order.

M o t h e r   G o o s e

Page 82

All Kinds of Kites

A kite is an object that flies in the air at the end of a string. Kites come in many different shapes. A delta kite is mostly a triangular shape. A box kite consists of squares, rectangles, or triangles.

Use the clues to find the shapes in the puzzle.

Across

Crossword answers: cube, cylinder, circle, rectangle, square, diamond, triangle, octagon, cone

Down

Word Bank	
octagon	diamond
triangle	rectangle
square	cylinder
circle	cube
cone	

Page 83

A Climb to the Top!

The first team to climb Mt. Everest arrived at the top on May 29, 1953.

Climb to the top of each mountain by changing one letter to make a new word.

cap
leg
peg, pet, met, men, ten
top, pop, pot, dot, dog, jog
map, mat, bat, bar, far

Answers will vary.

Page 84

Memorial Day

Memorial Day is a day set aside to remember all who have died while serving our country. It is observed on the last Monday in May.

Answer the questions using the words in the Word Bank.

Word Bank		
coast guard	marines	navy
military police	air force	army

1. soldiers who serve on land **a r m y**
2. soldiers who serve in the air **a i r   f o r c e**
3. soldiers who serve at sea **n a v y**
4. police that enforce laws in the military **m i l i t a r y   p o l i c e**
5. soldiers who serve at sea, on land, and in the air **m a r i n e s**
6. men in boats that protect our water borders **c o a s t   g u a r d**

To solve the riddle, fill in the blanks with the circled letters in order.

What rises in the morning and waves all day?

a   f l a g

Page 85

Favorite Fruit

A strawberry is a red, heart-shaped fruit. In most states, this delicious fruit is produced from May to November.

Unscramble the names of the fruits and circle them in the puzzle.

pplea
a p p l e

paergs
g r a p e s

erpa
p e a r

lnepppaie
p i n e a p p l e

aaannb
b a n a n a

anergo
o r a n g e

herrcy
c h e r r y

mlie
l i m e

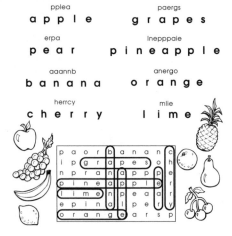

Page 86

Father's Day

Father's Day is the third Sunday in June. Celebrate this day by doing something special with your dad. Hidden in the picture are some symbols of America's favorite pastime. It is something you could do with your dad.

Color each space brown if the word makes the **short a** sound as in **dad**. Color each space blue if the word makes the **long a** sound as in **day**.

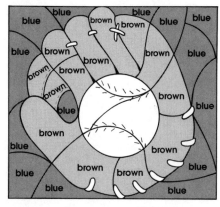

Page 87

Show Me the Sign

Helen Keller had a serious illness when she was very young that left her blind and deaf. Through sign language and braille, she learned to communicate. Helen Keller went on to college and then spent her life helping others.

Sign language is a way to communicate using your hands. Use the code to find another name for sign language.

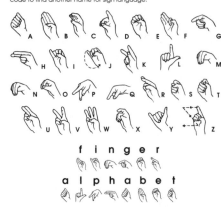

f i n g e r

a l p h a b e t

Page 88

Some Special Zoos

The Philadelphia Zoo was the first zoo in the United States. The Bronx Zoo is the largest city zoo.

Connect the dots next to the animals in alphabetical order from **a** to **z** to find the largest land animal that lives in the zoo.

What is the biggest ant? **a n e l e p h a n t**

Page 89

Enough for Everyone

Candy is a special treat. To make sure there is enough for everyone, we need more than just one piece of candy. One way to make more candy is to change the **y** to **i** and adding **es**.

Color the space red if you change the **y** to **i** and add **es** to make the word plural. Color the space blue if you just add **es** to make the word plural. Color the space yellow if you just add **s** to make the word plural.

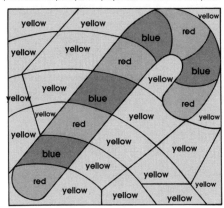

Page 90

One Nation

The Fourth of July is a celebration of our independence from England.

Use the code to fill in the missing letters. Then, to find out why it was said that George Washington had the largest family in America, write all the bolded letters in order on the blanks below.

1. V **a l l** e y   F **o r** g **e**
2. R **e** d **c** o **a** t s
3. P **h i l** a d e **l** p **h** i a
4. George   W **a s h** i n g t o n
5. f r **e e d o** m
6. R e v o l **u** t **i o n** a r y   W a r
7. A m **e** r **i** c a
8. P a t **r** i o t s
9. Un **c l e**   S **a m**
10. P a t **r i c k**   H e n **r** y

Code

a = [img]   b = [img]
c = [img]   d = [img]
e = [img]   g = [img]
h = [img]   i = [img]
l = [img]   m = [img]
n = [img]   o = [img]
p = [img]   r = [img]
s = [img]   t = [img]

He was the **f a t h e r   o f**
o u r   c o u n t r y!

Page 91

The Greatest Show on Earth!

P.T. Barnum was born on July 5, 1810. He is known for starting the most famous circus in America.

Use the clues to complete each word family puzzle. Then use the picture code to solve the riddle below.

1. broad
2. a woman getting married
3. next to
4. opposite from inside

```
        i d e
   1. w i d e
   2. b r i d e
   3. b e s i d e
4. o u t s i d e
```

1. more than one mouse
2. another word for two times
3. a suggestion

```
        i c e
1. m i c e
2. t w i c e
3. a d v i c e
```

1. ruler
2. something a bee does
3. after winter

```
      i n g
1. k i n g
2. s t i n g
3. s p r i n g
```

What happened to the kid who ran away with the circus? The police made him **b r i n g i t b a c k**!
☆ ★ ❋ ✦ ◆ ✿ ✹ ✦ ✹ ✱

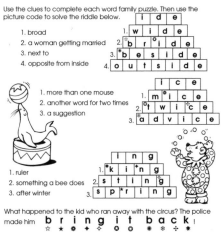

Page 92

The Great Watermelon Contest

In August, during the annual Watermelon Fest in Hope, Arkansas, a seed-spitting contest is held. The person who spits a seed the farthest wins. Awards are also given to the highest, straightest, and funniest seed-spitters.

Color each flag if you can make a word by adding the beginning sound next to the word family on the watermelon. The contestant with the most flags colored is the winner.

ap   c   cl   str   tr   br

aw   j   fl   str   th   gr

ate   c   pl   sk   st   w

ash   c   fl   tr   spl   sk

Page 93

Can You Picture This?

August is National Catfish Month. To celebrate use the Word Bank to make compound words with **fish**. These are the names of real fish, but they do not really look like these pictures!

Word Bank				
sword	trumpet	trunk	cat	hog
clown	hatchet	lion	sun	star

s t a r fish

h o g fish

l i o n fish

c l o w n fish

s w o r d fish

c a t fish

t r u m p e t fish

t r u n k fish

h a t c h e t fish

s u n fish

Page 94

Back to School!

August is when most students are returning to school.
Read each clue. Use the Word Bank to fill in the blanks.

Word Bank					
balloon	moose	book	cooking	spoon	cool
wood	choose	football	pool	tooth	poor

1. rhymes with goose — m o o s e
2. neither warm nor cold — c o o l
3. used for chewing — t o o t h
4. something you read — b o o k
5. a sport — f o o t b a l l
6. something filled with air — b a l l o o n
7. preparing food — c o o k i n g
8. used when eating — s p o o n
9. rhymes with lose — c h o o s e
10. opposite of rich — p o o r
11. rhymes with stood — w o o d
12. a place to swim — p o o l

To find out something about school, write the boxed letters in order on the blanks below.

S c h o o l   i s   c o o l !

Page 95

Days of the Week

The days of the week come from Latin words.
Unscramble each day of the week using its abbreviation for clues.

1. Fri.   Frdaiy   F r i d a y
2. Tues.   daTueys   T u e s d a y
3. Sat.   atSruyda S a t u r d a y
4. Thurs. yadtrhus T h u r s d a y
5. Sun.   ndauSy   S u n d a y
6. Mon.   ndanoMy   M o n d a y
7. Wed.   ndesWeyda W e d n e s d a y

Write the days of the week in order.

Sunday   Monday
Tuesday   Wednesday
Thursday   Friday
Saturday

Page 96

Months of the Year

Use the clues to write the names of the months below.

Word Bank					
January	March	May	July	September	November
February	April	June	August	October	December

1. What month is before June but after April? — M a y
2. What month is before August but after June? — J u l y
3. What month is before May but after March? — A p r i l
4. What month is before December but after October? — N o v e m b e r
5. What month is before March but after January? — F e b r u a r y
6. What month is before September but after July? — A u g u s t
7. What month is before April but after February? — M a r c h
8. What month is before July but after May? — J u n e
9. What month is before October but after August? — S e p t e m b e r

Page 97

A Jar of Many Colors

Jelly beans come in many colors like red, yellow, pink, orange, green, purple, and even black. Sometimes colors can have different names to describe them. For example, red is sometimes called cherry, yellow is lemon, pink is rose, purple is plum.

Color all the jelly beans with a color word on them red. Color all other jelly beans blue.

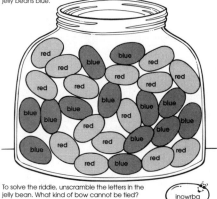

To solve the riddle, unscramble the letters in the jelly bean. What kind of bow cannot be tied?

a   r a i n b o w

inowrba

Page 98

Which Watch?

Learning to tell time is important. One thing to remember is that the small hand tells the hour and the large hand tells the minutes.

Write the time using number words.

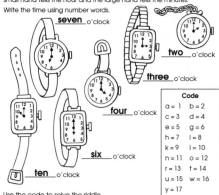

seven o'clock
two o'clock
three o'clock
four o'clock
six o'clock
ten o'clock

Code	
a = 1	b = 2
c = 3	d = 4
e = 5	g = 6
h = 7	i = 8
k = 9	l = 10
n = 11	o = 12
r = 13	t = 14
u = 15	w = 16
y = 17	

Use the code to solve the riddle.
What did the big watch hand say to the little watch hand?

"D o n t   g o   a w a y ,   I l l
 4   12   11   14   6   1   16   1   17   8   10   10

 b e   b a c k   i n   a n   h o u r"
 2 5   2 1 3 9   8 11   1 11   7 12 15 13

Page 99

A Castle Fit for a King

If you look carefully at buildings, you will notice they are full of different shapes. Follow the directions to find all the shapes in the castle.

Color the rectangles red. Color the triangles green. Color the circles yellow. Color the squares blue.

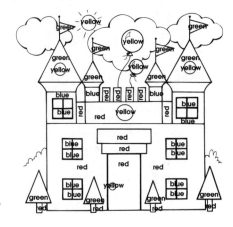

Page 100

Inching Along in Spring

Every spring you will see the inchworm crawling along. It crawls by pulling the back part of its body towards the front. Inchworms form loose cocoons and later appear as moths.

Circle the words in the top row with the vowel sound like **twig**.
Circle the words in the bottom row with the vowel sound like **rice**.

1	2	3	4	5	6	7
(big)	rice	lie	listen	(him)	pine	line
tie	(chick)	(dig)	ice	tie	(inch)	(pin)

8	9	10	11	12	13	14
(mike)	(nine)	wig	fin	(stripe)	(white)	pig
fix	napkin	(outside)	(rice)	pick	sick	(right)

Write the bolded letters in the correct blanks below to solve the tongue twister.

An   i n c r e d i b l e
     9 6 2 13 5 4 8 1 7 14

i n c h w o r m
6 9 2 13 16 10 11 8

i n c h e d   i n s i d e .
6 9 2 13 5 4   6 9 12 6 3 4

Page 101

Hopping Along

During the summer months, a pond is a hopping place.

Help the frog hop across the pond by hopping on the lily pads that are in the **op** word family and coloring them green. Start with hop.

Page 102

Fall Colors

In the fall, leaves of some trees turn bright colors before they die and fall to the ground.

Unscramble the words below. Color the leaves that have words that begin with **t** red. Color the leaves that have words that begin with **w** yellow. Color the leaves that have words that begin with **h** orange. Color the leaves that have words that begin with **f** green.

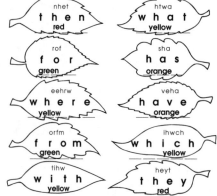

nhet — t h e n — red
htwa — w h a t — yellow
rof — f o r — green
sha — h a s — orange
eehrw — w h e r e — yellow
veha — h a v e — orange
orfm — f r o m — green
ihwch — w h i c h — yellow
tihw — w i t h — yellow
heyt — t h e y — red

Word Games: Grades 1–2

Page 103

Polar Bear

Polar bears live in the north along the frozen shores and icy waters of the Arctic Ocean. They have thick, white fur that blends in with ice and snow.

Help Susie Bear slide down the snowy maze to find her cub, Sam. Follow the words that make new compound words with **snow**.

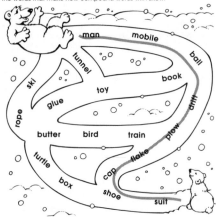

Page 104

How Many?

A body has many parts. There are two of some parts. Other parts have more than two. Write each word from the Word Bank in the appropriate space.

one

n o s e
h e a r t
m o u t h
t o n g u e

Word Bank	
ears	tongue
ribs	eyebrows
teeth	toes
elbows	mouth
heart	nose
eyes	fingers

more than two

two

e a r s
e y e s
e l b o w s
e y e b r o w s

r i b s
t e e t h
t o e s
f i n g e r s

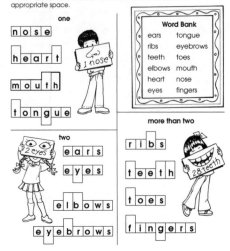

Page 105

X and 0

Tic-tac-toe means three in a row. Put an **x** on the words that go together in each game. Then circle each tic-tac-toe.

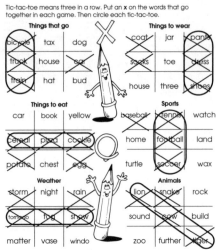

Things that go

bicycle	tax	dog
track	house	car
train	hat	bud

Things to wear

coat	jar	pants
socks	toe	dress
house	three	shoes

Things to eat

car	book	yellow
cereal	pizza	cookie
potato	chest	egg

Sports

baseball	tennis	watch
home	football	land
turtle	soccer	wax

Weather

storm	night	rain
tornado	fog	snow
matter	vase	windo

Animals

lion	snake	rock
sound	cow	build
zoo	further	tiger

Page 106

Feelings

Follow the directions written below the picture.

1. Draw a square around the face that is the opposite of **sad**.
2. Circle the the face that rhymes with brightened.
3. Draw two lines under the face that rhymes with **mad**.
4. Draw a triangle around the surprised face.
5. Put a X through the face that rhymes with **sad**.
6. Draw a heart around the face that is doing something that rhymes with **dawn**.

Page 107

Gum Balls

On each dotted line write a word that rhymes with the word on the gum ball.

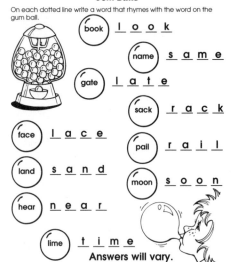

book — l o o k
name — s a m e
gate — l a t e
sack — r a c k
pail — r a i l
face — l a c e
land — s a n d
hear — n e a r
moon — s o o n
lime — t i m e

Answers will vary.

Page 108

What Sport Is It?

Use the clues to solve the puzzle.

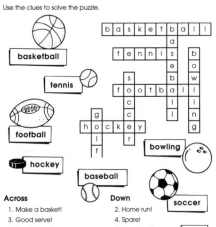

basketball

tennis

football

hockey

baseball

bowling

soccer

golf

Across

1. Make a basket!
3. Good serve!
6. Touchdown!
8. Shoot the puck!

Down

2. Home run!
4. Spare!
5. Head ball!
7. Hole in one!

Page 109

Holiday Fun

Use the clues to solve the riddle.

Word Bank		
Halloween	Thanksgiving	Valentines Day
Independence Day	Presidents' Day	

1. a day we celebrate the birthdays of Lincoln and Washington
2. a day when children in costumes go trick-or-treating
3. a day for giving hearts to people we care about
4. a holiday also called the Fourth of July
5. a day of feasting and giving thanks

1. **P r e s i d e n t s' D a y**
2. **H a l l o w e e n**
3. **V a l e n t i n e s D a y**
4. **I n d e p e n d e n c e D a y**
5. **T h a n k s g i v i n g**

What fruit has been known since man invented the calendar?

d a t e s

Word Games: Grades 1–2